D1095427

McGraw-Hill Series in
UNDERGRADUATE ASTRONOMY
Gerald S. Hawkins, Consulting Editor

HAWKINS: meteors, comets, and meteorites

the
physics
and
astronomy
of

GERALD S. HAWKINS

Boston University

Harvard College Observatory

Smithsonian Astrophysical Observatory

※ **meteors**
※ **comets**
and
meteorites

McGraw-Hill Book Company
New York • San Francisco • Toronto • London

TO DOROTHY AND LISETTE

PREFACE

This book forms part of a series covering the broad area of astronomy, astrophysics, and space science. Each book attempts to fulfill the need of an undergraduate student studying astronomy or space-related subjects. Although written primarily for a junior- or senior-year undergraduate in the physical sciences, the present work should also provide a useful reference for more advanced students who wish to augment their knowledge in this field.

It has been necessary to divide the subject matter into rather broad areas of interest in order to cover all topics in a few short monographs. This book deals with what might be called "interplanetary material," the region between the planets. Within this area, I have concentrated more on the interplanetary objects that have direct contact with the Earth, such as meteors and meteorites. This is primarily because our knowledge of these objects is somewhat greater than our knowledge of the objects that we cannot reach at present. Thus comets occupy two chapters out of nine, although in their connection with meteors comets are mentioned in many of the other chapters in the book. This division is roughly representative of our present fund of knowledge concerning comets and meteors.

Meteorites and tektites have been included in a separate chapter since they are an important component of interplanetary material. Our knowledge of meteorites has increased considerably during the last decade, particularly in the areas of chemical abundances, radio dating, and mineralogy. I have not covered these topics in great detail, concentrating rather on the astronomy of meteorites, on their relation to the Earth, and on their interest from the point of view of space science.

An appendix has been included with some questions relating to the text. These form a basic tool for assessing the study program if the book is used as a college text. For a more advanced reader, the questions will show the type of problem that might readily come to mind as he goes through the text. For the interested layman or non-scientist, the problems may be ignored with impunity.

Gerald S. Hawkins

CONTENTS

❋ 1 ❋   **introduction**

In historic times meteors and comets were regarded with super-stition. As a meteor particle moved through the upper atmosphere, the streak of light was thought to be a star falling from the firma-ment, and this viewpoint is embodied today in the popular term "shooting star." Comets remain visible in the nighttime sky for several weeks or months as they pass by the Earth in space. The pale tenuous nature of the tail gives them a ghostly appearance and is probably responsible to a large extent for their awesome reputation. Halley's Comet appeared in the sky just before the Battle of Hastings in 1066 and was interpreted as a portent of disaster for the English armies. The same comet appeared 1,110 years earlier at the time of the assassination of Julius Caesar. According to Plutarch, the apparition was a celestial comment on the black deed.

Some of the earliest records of meteor activity are contained in the ancient records of China, Korea, and Japan. Meteors can be seen, of course, on any clear night, but the ancient chroniclers noted only spectacular events when the sky was filled with streaks of light. Sometimes as many as 10,000 meteors can be seen during an hour. Under these conditions a very active meteor shower, or meteor storm, is taking place. Some of the more notable events of the past 2,000 years are given in Table 1.1. The terse comment of the chronicler is, unfortunately, the only information that we have available on these events. Careful research, however, has shown that at least some of the showers are related to meteor showers visible at the present time.

The nature of comets and meteors is now well understood, and the new knowledge has quickly dispersed the old superstitions. The comet is a conglomerate of ices several miles in diameter that moves in an elliptical orbit in the solar system. As the comet ap-proaches the sun, solar radiation vaporizes the ices, and gases are forced along the tail of the comet by the radiation pressure of sun-light. Small solid fragments are embedded in the icy nucleus of the comet and become detached as the comet vaporizes. The chem-ical composition of the particles is not known with any certainty. Presumably they are composed of stony minerals such as silica, with perhaps some grains of nickel-iron and carbon. Meteoroids, formed of the nonvolatile compounds, follow a path in space that is close to the original orbit of the comet, for at least several years after detachment from the nucleus. Gravitational disturbances and other

TABLE 1.1 NOTABLE METEOR EVENTS

DATE (Julian Calendar)	DESCRIPTION	CHRONICLE
687 B.C. Mar. 23	Stars fell like a shower	Han-shu Pên-chi (China)
104 A.D. Feb.–Mar.	Many stars fell like a shower, but did not reach the earth	Munhŏn-piko (Korea)
308 A.D. Jan. 20	Stars flew and scattered, trembling	T'ien-wên-chih (China)
464 A.D. Mar.–Apr.	Countless meteors flew west till morning	T'ien-wên-chih (China)
685 A.D. Nov. 24	Heaven stirred, stars fell like a shower	Mizu Kogami (Japan)
931 A.D. Oct. 15	Many stars flew, crossing each other	Ssŭ-tien-k'ao (China)
1363 A.D. May–June	Stars fought each other in the middle air	Munhŏn-piko (Korea)
1533 A.D. Nov. 3	Stars fell like a shower and made the heavens red	Lu-an-fu-chih (China)
1642 A.D. Summer	Stars flew like the weaving	T'ien-wên-chih (China)

effects later spread the meteoroid particles over an ever-increasing volume of space. In this monograph I shall begin by discussing the phenomenon of meteors and the relationship between meteors and comets. I shall discuss the nature of comets in the later chapters.

In meteor science, as in other areas of science, new terms have been invented by research workers as the need arose. There has therefore been some slight confusion in nomenclature from one authority to another. In 1961 the commission on meteors and meteorites of the International Astronomical Union helped to resolve this difficulty by adopting a number of standard definitions for the English, French, Russian, and German languages.

The term *meteor* is a general term to describe the whole phenomenon associated with the entry into the Earth's atmosphere of a solid particle from space. In particular, it describes the flash of light produced by the interaction and also the ionization generated in the upper atmosphere. The word can serve as a noun and also as an adjective. General usage has thus given the word a very broad meaning, and other words are needed when we become more specific. A *meteoroid* is the solid object moving in interplanetary space which, on entering the Earth's atmosphere, produces the phenomenon of a meteor. There are, of course, other solid objects in the solar system—comets, planets, and asteroids—and it is necessary to distinguish the meteoroid from these. One can adequately define a meteoroid in terms of size. It is an object that is considerably larger than an atom or a molecule but considerably smaller than the nucleus of a comet. It thus lies in the size range from a few microns (10^{-4} cm) in diameter to a few meters. A *meteorite* is a solid object that has reached the surface of the Earth without being completely vaporized in its passage through the atmosphere. The object is, of course, a natural and not an artificial satellite. The term *micrometeorite* refers to a special form of meteorite, an object of small size that completely melts on entering the atmosphere but does not vaporize. If the diameter of the particle is approximately 100 μ or less, the heat generated by passage through the atmosphere is radiated from the surface of the object, and no vaporization takes place. After it has been slowed down by the atmosphere, the droplet solidifies and falls to the Earth's surface as a small spherule.

A meteor *train* is a glowing column of light that is left in the path of a meteoroid. The train persists for a period of a second up to several minutes, and the glowing column hangs as a long line in the sky. If the train phenomenon is of very short duration, it is classified as a *wake*. In general, the wake phenomenon persists for a shorter period than the passage of the meteoroid through the upper atmosphere and appears as a very short tail following the meteoroid. The meteoroid also leaves behind an invisible *trail* of positive ions, electrons, and atoms. The electrons in the trail can be detected by radar.

When meteor particles enter the atmosphere in parallel paths, the effect is called a meteor *shower*. However, the word "shower" is now falling into disuse since it implies a much higher rate of appearance than normally occurs. "Shower" is being supplanted by the word "stream," which describes a group of meteor particles moving with nearly identical paths in interplanetary space and distributed fairly uniformly along the orbit. Particles occurring in great numbers are referred to as a *swarm*. The Earth passing through a swarm encounters many meteors, and a meteor *storm* is seen.

Much of our information on meteors has come from visual observers who plotted the courses of meteors and estimated their times of flight. Visual observations have now been supplanted by photographic and radio techniques for the determination of the trajectory through the atmosphere. Visual observations are, however, still useful for estimations of the rate of appearance of meteors in a stream, and for projects where the observer works in conjunction with photographic or radio equipment. The standard measurement of brightness is still based on the visual scale, the magnitude that would be recorded by a visual observer.

Two students at Göttingen University were the first to make a scientific study of meteors. In 1798 the two students, Heinrich Brandes and Johann Benzenberg, observed meteors simultaneously from two different townships. When the same meteor was observed, the trail appeared to be displaced against the background of the stars when viewed from the two sites. The parallactic displacement gave a measure of the height of the meteor, and from estimates of time of flight the speed could also be determined. This triangulation method forms the basis of all multistation visual and photographic observations.

Consider two observers, *O* and *O'*, as shown in Figure 1.1. The straight trajectory of the meteor must lie in the plane drawn through *O*. Similarly, another plane can be drawn through the meteor and the observer *O'*. The path of the meteor is therefore defined by the intersection of these two planes.

It is convenient to project the two planes onto the celestial sphere, for this is what the visual observer does in practice. The celestial sphere is an imaginary sphere drawn at infinity on which the stars are supposed to be hung. The baseline between the observers is infinitesimally small when compared to the sphere. When projected, the two planes will cut the sphere in great circles as shown in Figure 1.2. Observer O sees the meteor projected at A, and O' sees it at B. When the two great circles are extended backward along the path of the meteor, they intersect. This pole of intersection is the point where the vector representing the space trajectory of the meteor would cut the celestial sphere. It is called the *radiant point* of the meteor.

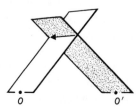

FIGURE 1.1   Two visual observers and a meteor path.

Meteoroids in a stream move in parallel paths; thus a number of trajectories will appear in the upper atmosphere that are parallel to each other. All the meteors will have a common radiant point, and one observer alone will find that the meteor paths intersect when projected backward. This effect is similar to the perspective vanishing point of parallel lines. Since the parallel trajectories of a meteor stream are governed by the orbit in space, the radiant point remains fixed with respect to the stars. It thus rises above the horizon owing to the Earth's rotation, crosses the celestial meridian due south of the observer, and sets in the west. During the course of a night the radiant moves with the stars and remains within a certain constellation. It has been common practice to name a meteor stream from the constellation in which the radiant is located or, in the case of duplication, from the star that is nearest to the radiant point. Thus we have the Perseids with the radiant point in Perseus and the Geminids with the radiant point in Gemini.

The visual rate is taken to be the number of meteors that an observer would see on a clear moonless night. It is tacitly assumed that he has average vision and an unobstructed sky. Of course the visual rate can never be a precise figure, because it depends upon many uncontrolled factors. More meteors are seen, for example, when one looks at an altitude of approximately 50 deg, since the observing cone then contains a greater volume of the upper atmosphere. The rate also depends upon the angle of altitude of the radiant point. More meteors are seen when the radiant is closest to the zenith, for then the area of atmosphere under observation is more nearly perpendicular to the direction of arrival of the meteor particles. Notwithstanding the utmost precautions, two apparently average observers can differ considerably in their estimates of the hourly rate. Discrepancies of up to 50 per cent are sometimes encountered.

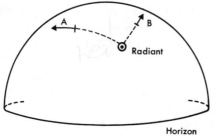

FIGURE 1.2   The meteor path as projected on the celestial sphere by two spaced observers.

On any night during the year under average conditions an observer may expect to see 5 to 10 meteors hr^{-1} that do not belong to any particular stream. On certain calendar dates the annual streams occur, and then the rate increases. For example, on August 12 the Perseids provide from 40 to 60 meteors hr^{-1}, and the rate for the Orionids on October 22 is approximately 15.

A visual observer estimates the brightness of a meteor by comparing it directly with a star. Thus the faintest meteor that one might expect to see is on the visual threshold at magnitude +6. In practice, owing to the movement of the object, it is very difficult to see a meteor as faint as this, and the more realistic visual limit is magnitude +5. The brightness of a meteor increases by a factor of 2.512 for each step of 1 magnitude. If the meteor emits I ergs sec^{-1}, the magnitude M is given by

$$M = 24.3 - 2.5 \log_{10}I \qquad (1.1)$$

A meteor of zero magnitude is therefore 100 times brighter than a meteor of magnitude +5. Meteors brighter than zero are assigned negative magnitudes. At −4.4 the meteor would be as bright as the planet Venus; at −12.6 it would be as bright as the full moon.

Most countries influenced by scientific culture have had organized teams of visual observers at some time or other. The American Meteor Society, under the direction of C. P. Olivier, has collected valuable data from more than 100 amateurs in the United States. On the basis of this work it is now possible to give a fair estimate of the hourly rate of meteors to be expected on any night of the year. The visual rates under ideal conditions are given in Table 1.2. In general, one cannot expect to see as many meteors as indicated by the corrected A.M.S. data, since these rates are based to a considerable extent on observations made in the clear air of desert regions and on mountain tops. A slight haze, moonlight, glare from a city, and partial cloud cover will all tend to reduce the rate. Whereas the faintest star visible under ideal conditions might be +6.5, the limiting magnitude in general seldom exceeds +6.0 or +5.5. A loss of one magnitude reduces the rate by a factor of approximately 3.4. Thus the numbers in the table should be divided by a factor of 2 to give more representative values to be expected under average conditions. Usually more meteors are seen after midnight, and the table has been drawn up for the hour between 3 and 4 A.M. For the month of December the selected hour is between 2 and 3 A.M. Figures in parentheses have been interpolated.

The A.M.S. has also provided information on the number of extremely bright meteors that one is likely to see. The average rate of meteors brighter than a given magnitude M is given in Table 1.3. These figures apply, of course, to nights when no major meteor stream is active. It can be seen that one must wait 76 hours before one sees a meteor of magnitude −5. For a meteor brighter than −10 the "waiting time" is 7,600 hours. Bright meteors are therefore extremely rare, and many years of systematic observation have to be made before the watcher can be sure of seeing these spectacular objects. The problem is a statistical one, though, and the "waiting time" is an average taken over a long period. There is of course always the same small finite chance of seeing a bright meteor whenever one takes a look at the sky.

Between 1931 and 1933 a group of observers under the sponsorship of Harvard and Cornell Universities was sent to Arizona pro-

TABLE 1.2 **HOURLY METEOR RATE AT 3 A.M. UNDER IDEAL CONDITIONS**

DAY	JAN.	FEB.	MAR.	APR.	MAY	JUNE	JULY	AUG.	SEPT.	OCT.	NOV.	DEC.
1	19	24	12	10	13	14	9	37	10	10	15	22
2	33	3	(8)	9	14	6	16	32	18	12	16	18
3	30	21	5	12	19	8	21	22	15	18	23	30
4	20	16	13	5	19	10	15	32	10	19	(17)	19
5	17	(16)	5	7	18	4	26	14	23	17	11	18
6	16	16	14	4	19	9	14	20	22	15	12	19
7	(16)	4	11	9	18	8	21	21	19	18	17	36
8	17	10	10	5	15	13	19	35	16	20	10	18
9	25	(11)	14	12	18	16	32	33	14	17	15	12
10	(20)	12	11	21	12	21	18	42	14	12	11	29
11	14	12	11	8	25	(17)	22	66	34	23	19	25
12	26	11	(12)	11	26	13	13	39	(22)	18	15	83
13	19	19	13	20	21	20	20	32	10	20	14	44
14	12	13	26	8	9	7	35	29	13	17	21	30
15	11	13	11	10	10	18	9	17	13	21	25	18
16	20	9	5	9	13	(17)	24	16	28	20	(20)	23
17	16	3	11	7	12	(16)	22	26	13	20	15	18
18	20	(7)	17	18	12	(15)	11	18	8	21	21	18
19	12	22	8	7	11	14	13	19	19	24	13	22
20	16	15	8	10	12	31	23	24	18	25	13	17
21	19	(15)	10	14	(13)	13	14	22	25	41	31	16
22	17	(15)	12	14	(13)	23	33	32	25	25	28	7
23	12	(15)	6	9	14	40	17	24	21	25	19	27
24	12	15	2	6	20	5	36	11	20	19	15	16
25	14	9	8	14	14	9	31	21	19	17	(17)	23
26	12	12	6	8	21	12	34	22	17	22	(19)	16
27	10	16	8	11	9	22	24	24	27	28	21	28
28	(14)	8	(5)	14	20	20	28	23	15	22	16	15
29	16	15	1	13	7	14	23	17	10	10	30	19
30	20	. . .	12	10	28	18	29	20	11	22	15	25
31	14	. . .	(11)	. . .	(21)	. . .	30	15	. . .	22	. . .	11

vided with equipment to increase their accuracy. They looked at the sky through a grid of iron rods which enabled them to read off directly the coordinates of the meteor path. The observatory was something like a wooden "doghouse" with a lattice roof. Other observers looked at the sky through a rocking mirror that aided in the measurement of velocity. The normal of the mirror was made to precess several times per second, so that a star appeared as a small ellipse when viewed through the mirror. When a meteor moved across the field of view, the straight path was converted into a series of loops. By counting the number of loops, the observer could measure the duration of flight of the meteor and hence find the velocity.

TABLE 1.3   AVERAGE INFLUX RATE OF BRIGHT METEORS

Magnitude M	−5	−6	−7	−8	−9	−10	−15
Hourly rate N	1.3×10^{-2}	5.1×10^{-3}	2.0×10^{-3}	8.1×10^{-4}	3.2×10^{-4}	1.3×10^{-4}	1.3×10^{-6}

In Canada, members of the Royal Astronomical Society of Canada and others have been organized in a team to work in conjunction with radar equipment. Visual observers have provided important data on the major meteor streams. In particular, it has been possible to correlate the visual magnitude with the strength and duration of the radar echo. Similar joint observing programs have been carried out in England and Sweden, although the archenemy of visual observers, the weather, has curtailed the programs to some extent. The application of radar methods to the study of meteors will be described in more detail in a later chapter.

It has been possible to extend the range of a visual observer below magnitude +5. With good binoculars, or a telescope with wide aperture and low magnification, meteors as faint as +10 can be seen. Systematic observations were made by the Arizona meteor expedition, and part of the time the rocking mirror was used with a telescope. Telescopic observations from two spaced stations have been made in Czechoslovakia, and a considerable amount of data has been accumulated. Telescopic observations are, however, very tedious to make. With most instruments the rate is low (less than 5 meteors hr^{-1}) owing to the small field of view, and fatigue rapidly sets in. Under these conditions optical illusions can at times develop, and an observer may see things that are not really there. During one of the scientific expeditions to Antarctica an ambitious telescopic program was carried out. At times the observers were reporting hundreds of meteors per hour as seen through the telescope. Subsequent observations in Antarctica have failed to confirm the result, and we must infer that the original observations were false. The disadvantage of the telescope can be overcome by using a television image converter. By electronic amplification the image of a large part of the sky can be intensified, and faint stars and meteors are then viewed on a television screen. This new technique has not yet been used to any great extent.

At the other end of the magnitude scale we enter the regime of fireballs and bolides. In the past some astronomers made a distinction between these two phenomena; a fireball was a meteor bright enough to be reported by the "man in the street," and a bolide was a very bright meteor that exploded in the upper atmosphere. The International Astronomical Union has now defined the terms to mean one and the same thing. A fireball or bolide is a meteor with a luminosity that equals or exceeds that of the brightest planets, and it is therefore brighter than −5 on the visual scale.

Very little is known about fireballs owing to their extreme rarity. It is suspected that they are not related to the meteoroid particles and, therefore, have not been ejected by comets. An object weighing some 200 lb is required to produce a fireball as bright as the full moon. It is difficult to conceive how the loose dust associated with the cometary nucleus could be collected together to form such a massive object. More probably a fireball object is related to the asteroids or minor planets. There is a zone between Mars and Jupiter where thousands of fragments are located. Although most of them have nearly circular orbits, a fair percentage have elliptical orbits that carry them across the orbit of the Earth. Small spherical asteroids, or minor planets, are also found in the zone. Ceres, for example, is approximately 480 miles in diameter, and Pallas and Vesta are comparable in size. It is thought that two or more asteroids similar to Ceres have collided in the past. The irregular-shaped asteroids are presumed to be the results of such a collision.

Calculations show that a fireball as bright as the full moon will penetrate the atmosphere and deposit a solid object weighing some 20 lb on the surface of the Earth. Following the previous definition, the fireball deposits a *meteorite*. The objects recovered after a fireball or bolide has appeared in the sky lend support to the theory that meteorites are related to asteroidal fragments. Such solid objects are composed of either stone or nickel-iron and are essentially what would be expected from a broken planet.

It is important that we distinguish between meteoroid and meteorite. A meteoroid is a dustball that has been dislodged from a comet; a meteorite is a solid chunk from the asteroid zone. This distinction is emphasized clearly by the two following interlocking facts. All meteorites that have been observed to fall have fallen on dates when no meteor shower was active or have followed a trajectory different from meteors in a stream. No member of a meteor stream has ever been observed to fall to Earth, and in this are included the intense storms, such as the Giacobinids or Leonids, when many thousands of meteors have appeared during the course of an hour.

The orbit of a meteoroid around the sun is governed by Kepler's three laws:

1. The orbit of a meteoroid is an ellipse with the sun at one focus.
2. Each meteoroid revolves so that the line joining it to the sun sweeps over equal areas in equal intervals of time.
3. The square of the period is proportional to the cube of the semimajor axis, or $P^2 = a^3$, where the period is in units of the Earth's year and the semimajor axis is in astronomical units (AU).

Kepler's unwritten fourth law gives the speed of an object V (in kilometers per second) as a function of its distance from the sun, r (in astronomical units):

$$V^2 = 886 \left(\frac{2}{r} - \frac{1}{a} \right) \tag{1.2}$$

For a parabolic orbit $a = \infty$, and the velocity of an object in a parabolic orbit is 42 km sec^{-1} when crossing the Earth's orbit.

The pure geometry of an ellipse has several interesting applications in orbital work. The perihelion and aphelion distance, the semilatus rectum and semiminor axis can all be expressed in terms of the eccentricity of the ellipse, as shown in Figure 1.3. The distance between the two foci is equal to $2ae$. For a circle, $e = 0$, and

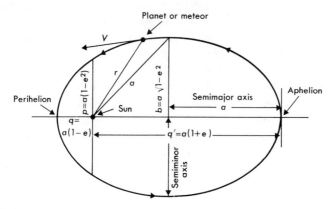

FIGURE 1.3   The geometry of an ellipse. *From Meteor Science and Engineering by D. W. R. McKinley. Copyright, 1961. McGraw-Hill Book Company. Used by permission.*

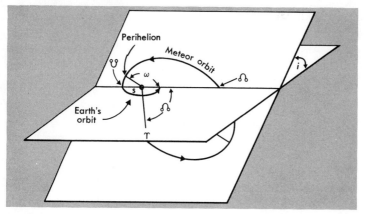

FIGURE 1.4   The orbit of a meteor. *From Meteor Science and Engineering by D. W. R. McKinley. Copyright, 1961. McGraw-Hill Book Company. Used by permission.*

the two foci coincide. As e approaches 1.0, the ellipse becomes more and more elongated, and for a given value of a the aphelion point moves further away from the sun. When $e = 1.0$, the orbit degenerates into a parabola, and the aphelion point is located at infinity. For hyperbolic orbits, $e > 1.0$, and a becomes negative.

The plane of a meteor orbit is not necessarily in the plane of the orbit of the Earth. A typical example is shown in Figure 1.4. In addition to a and e, three angular elements are required to define the orbit in space. The angle of tilt between the two planes is given by the inclination i. The two planes intersect along the line of nodes. This line defines the plane of the meteor orbit with respect to the sun, and the longitude of the ascending node Ω specifies the direction of the line of nodes. It is measured with respect to the sun, and the line to the vernal equinox is taken as the zero direction. The argument of perihelion ω gives the direction of the perihelion point. It is an angle measured around the orbit in the direction of motion of the meteoroid from the ascending node.

☀ **2** ☀

the
meteor
process

A meteoroid meets the atmosphere of the Earth at a speed between 11 and 72 km sec^{-1}. A tremendous amount of energy is released by this collision with the atmosphere, in the same way that energy is released by spacecraft during the period of reentry. With modern technology it is possible to dissipate the heat of the collision, in the case of spacecraft, in order to bring the astronaut safely down to Earth. For a meteoroid, however, Nature is not protective, and the process results in the total destruction of the meteoroid. It is a strange irony that a particle of such low density and with such a small crushing strength should be subjected to one of the most drastic treatments that Nature can provide.

As the meteoroid enters the atmosphere, it collides with atoms and molecules. Some of the air particles are reflected from the surface, and others are absorbed and trapped in the meteoroid. The atoms that are trapped dissipate their kinetic energy. Some of the energy goes toward heating up the solid structure of the meteoroid, and some is radiated away into space. Sputtering can also take place when the energy of collision dislodges an atom from the solid surface of the meteoroid. At a height of approximately 110 km, the heating of the meteoroid becomes intense. Atoms boil off from the surface with thermal velocities of about 1 km sec^{-1}, but these atoms still possess the forward motion of the meteoroid and are therefore ejected into the atmosphere with a relative velocity of up to 72 km sec^{-1}. As the meteor atoms collide with those in the atmosphere, excitation and ionization are produced. A glowing envelope surrounding the moving meteoroid is then seen, with a long trail of electrons and positive ions behind the meteoroid.

The process is complicated by fragmentation. During the interaction with the atmosphere, minute fragments are dislodged from the meteoroid. These act as very small meteoroids, becoming heated and vaporizing as they pass through the air. To describe the process quantitatively, the total effect produced by these separate particles as they become detached must be taken into account. As a further complication, the physical nature of the individual particles is not known. The interaction depends to a great extent on the actual shapes and sizes of the fragments and of the original meteoroid. A large object will tend to form a thin molten layer on the surface from which evaporation takes place and from which droplets are shed. A small object will tend to melt completely and move through the air as an incandescent droplet. These and other considerations

make the complete formal solution of the equations of the meteor
process an impossibility. However, approximations can be made
that are very useful in helping scientists to understand the phenomena.

The early observations of Brandes and Benzenberg were an
immediate proof that the atmosphere of the Earth extended up to
a height of at least 60 miles. Around 1800 many scientists thought
that the atmosphere extended perhaps no higher than the water-
vapor clouds. Yet the fact that meteors were flashing into view as
the result of frictional heating showed that there must be considerable amounts of air at these heights. In the 1930s observations of
meteors were conducted with the primary purpose of studying the
upper atmosphere. From the rate of change of speed it was possible
to make an estimate of the density of the air. However, these estimates were uncertain owing to the complicated nature of the
meteoroid itself and the lack of an exact theory. At the present time
it is more convenient to accept measurements of the upper atmosphere made by rockets and satellites and to use the interaction
process to study the meteoroid itself.

Consider a solid of sphere of radius r passing through the atmosphere with velocity v. The cross-sectional area is πr^2, and the mass
of air swept up per second is $\pi r^2 \rho v$, where ρ is the atmospheric
density. At the beginning of the trail the air atoms impinge directly
on the surface of the meteoroid, either sticking to it or being
reflected from it. In either case, momentum is transferred from the
meteoroid to the air, and from the law of conservation of momentum we may write the drag equation

$$m \frac{dv}{dt} = \Gamma \pi r^2 \rho v^2 \tag{2.1}$$

where m is the mass of the meteoroid and Γ is the drag coefficient.
Since the mass of a sphere of density δ is $\frac{4}{3}\pi r^3 \delta$, the drag equation
becomes

$$\frac{dv}{dt} = \frac{3\Gamma \rho v^2}{4r\delta} \tag{2.2}$$

When all the air is trapped in the meteoroid, $\Gamma = 1$. For a sphere
under conditions of free molecular or atomic flow, the drag co-

efficient is also unity. Thus $\Gamma = 1$ is a good approximation for a sphere at the initial part of the trail. In the lower atmosphere an air cap forms, and the drag coefficient decreases to an approximate value of 0.5. For an average visual meteor the position of maximum light occurs in a transition zone between free-flow and air-cap, and the drag coefficient has an intermediate value.

A certain fraction Λ of the impinging air is trapped in the meteoroid and transfers kinetic energy at a rate of $\frac{1}{2}\Lambda\pi r^2 \rho v^3$ ergs sec^{-1}. Most of this energy goes toward melting and vaporizing the meteoroid. From the law of conservation of energy, the rate of vaporization can be expressed as

$$\zeta \frac{dm}{dt} = \frac{1}{2} \Lambda\pi r^2 \rho v^3 \tag{2.3}$$

where ζ is the ablation coefficient. For a stony material such as silica, $\zeta = 8 \times 10^{10}$ ergs g^{-1} is a good approximation.

The atoms that evaporate from the meteoroid are moving with a forward velocity of some 30 km sec^{-1}. Each atom is therefore injected into the atmosphere with an energy of about 150 ev. The meteor atoms become ionized and excited as they collide with the air, and photons are emitted as the excited atoms return to their normal state. The energy released per second by the vapor is is $\frac{1}{2}(dm/dt)v^2$. A certain fraction of this energy τ is converted into light, so that the luminous energy emitted per second I may be written

$$I = \frac{1}{2}\left(\frac{dm}{dt}\right)v^2\tau \tag{2.4}$$

The luminous efficiency τ must take into account the light emitted by all types of atoms from all excitation states. It is found to depend on the velocity of the meteoroid, so that $\tau = 2.0 \times 10^{-10}\ v$ ergs sec^{-1}, where v is in units of centimeters per second. The magnitude of the meteor can be found by substituting for I in equation (1.1).

The vaporized atoms can also become ionized during the collision process. The ionizing probability β is the probability that one meteor atom will produce an electron-ion pair. Thus the number of atoms evaporated per second is $\frac{1}{\mu}\frac{dm}{dt}$, where μ is the average mass of a meteor atom. The number of ion pairs produced per second is

$\dfrac{\beta}{\mu}\dfrac{dm}{dt}$. It is convenient to talk of the number of electrons produced per centimeter of trail. This number is known as the line density q. Because the positive ions do not reflect radio waves to any great extent, it is the line density of electrons that is important in radar work. Since the meteoroid travels a distance of v cm sec^{-1}, the following may be written:

$$q = \frac{1}{v}\frac{\beta}{\mu}\frac{dm}{dt} \tag{2.5}$$

The ionizing probability must include the effects of all types of atoms present in the meteoroid. The greatest contribution to ionization comes from atoms of silicon, iron, and sodium. A detailed calculation gives the following approximate relation: $\beta = 2.0 \times 10^{-26} v^{3.4}$, with v in units of cm sec^{-1}.

The meteor process is not very efficient in the production of light. From the value of τ in Equation (2.4) one can deduce that 0.01 per cent of the kinetic energy is converted into light in the visible spectrum. The value of luminous efficiency has been measured experimentally by firing iron spheres into the upper atmosphere at velocities comparable to those of meteors. The fact that τ varies with velocity has been deduced from theoretical considerations. The luminous efficiency will increase by a factor of 7 from the slowest meteors, with $v = 12$ km sec^{-1}, to the fastest meteors, with $v = 72$ km sec^{-1}. The ionizing probability has been derived from a detailed quantum mechanical calculation for the atom of sodium. It was necessary to assume the chemical composition of the meteoroids before the effective value of β could be derived. The fraction of kinetic energy spent in ionization is even smaller than the fraction used to produce light. If it is assumed that an energy of 7 ev is required to produce each ion pair, then the percentage of energy used for ionization is 0.001 per cent. Thus we may write for slow meteors (velocity 12 km sec^{-1}) that the kinetic energy is divided between heat, light, and ionization in the following approximate ratio: $10^5{:}10{:}1$. For fast meteors (velocity 72 km sec^{-1}) the division of energy is in the ratio $10^5{:}10^2{:}5$.

Assuming an ideal atmosphere with uniform temperature, so that the density of the atmosphere decreases exponentially with height, the variation of light from a meteor can be written in a very succinct form. After several processes of differentiation and integration, the intensity may be expressed in terms of the intensity at maximum light I_{max}. The equation governing the variation of the light is

$$\frac{I}{I_{max}} = \frac{9}{4} \frac{\rho}{\rho_{max}} \left(1 - \frac{\rho}{3\rho_{max}}\right)^2 \tag{2.6}$$

where ρ_{max} is the air density at the point of maximum light. When plotted against air density or height, Equation (2.6) gives a curve which is known as the *classical light curve*. The same equation also governs the ratio of q/q_{max} where q_{max} is the electron line density at maximum ionization. This equation is remarkable in that it predicts a light curve that is independent of all the physical properties of the meteoroid. It does not depend upon the initial mass, the composition, the velocity, or the angle of approach. For bright meteors that resemble the model assumed here, that of a solid sphere, the classical light curve gives a good prediction of the variation of light. Three examples of bright meteors are given in Figure 2.1. The anomalous behavior of the third meteor is due to an explosion which took place and invalidated the theory from that point onward.

Although bright meteors follow the classical theory, faint meteors do not. In cooperation with R. B. Southworth I have studied the light curves of 361 meteors photographed over the White Sands Desert in New Mexico. The photographs were taken with two Super-Schmidt cameras able to record meteors down to a magnitude of $+4$. Figure 2.2 shows the summary of results when the light curves of all the meteors were plotted. The open circle, representing the position of maximum light for each meteor, is used as a reference point. The dots represent the beginning or end of a meteor as recorded on the photograph. The difference in height between the end point and maximum light was determined from the photograph. It was also possible to measure the decrease in magnitude between maximum light and the end point. Thus with brightness and height as coordinates we were able to plot the data for 361 meteors and compare the points with the theory.

The results indicate a serious breakdown of the classical theory. In general, the points are located inside the theoretical light curve

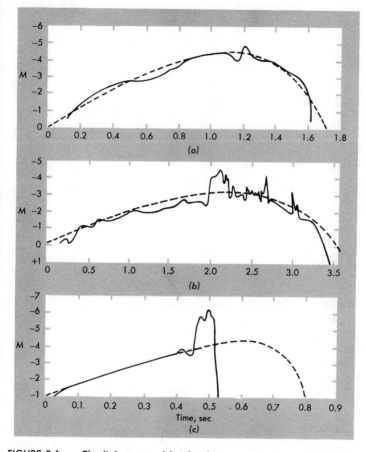

FIGURE 2.1   The light curve of bright photographic meteors. Solid lines, observed light curves of three bright meteors; dashed lines, theoretical light curves. Velocities: (a) 36 km sec^{-1}; (b) 25 km sec^{-1}; (c) 69 km sec^{-1}. *Courtesy L. G. Jacchia.*

on this diagram. The meteor trails are shorter than those predicted by the theory; clearly it does not apply to meteors in the visual range (magnitude +5 to 0), and reasons for the breakdown must be sought.

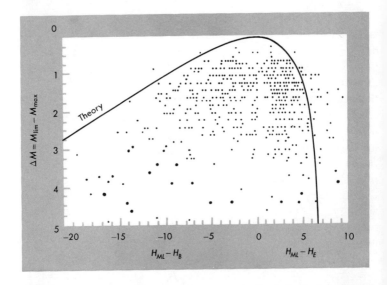

FIGURE 2.2   Theoretical light curve compared with the beginning and end points of a random selection of Super-Schmidt meteors. H_{ML} = height at maximum light; H_B = height at beginning of trail; H_E = height at end of trail. *From Meteor Science and Engineering by D. W. R. McKinley. Copyright, 1961. McGraw-Hill Book Company. Used by permission.*

The unusual shortness of the faint meteors can be explained by the fragmentation hypothesis. If the meteoroid breaks up into a number of small fragments upon entering the atmosphere, the conditions of the classical theory do not apply. The small fragments will burn up more rapidly because they are ejected into the atmosphere at heights lower than normal. They are carried down on the parent body through the fringe of the atmosphere and become dislodged when the denser layers of the atmosphere are reached.

There is further evidence for the fragmentation hypothesis. A meteor does not move as a "starlike" point of light. A visual observer, of course, will see the meteor as a streak, whether the meteoroid is a moving point or is slightly elongated. This effect is due to the persistence of vision of the eye where the image of the fast-moving object is smeared out on the retina. Tracer bullets give the impression of moving streaks, but if one could follow them accurately by moving the eyes, they would appear as points of light. Accurate measurements, however, show that a meteor is not a point. The ball of light surrounding the meteoroid is elongated, and a small tail moves across the sky behind the point of light. This tail, or wake, is caused by the microscopic fragments that have been dislodged from the meteoroid and lag behind the motion of the larger object. Sometimes the fragments can be separated from the meteoroid by as much as several kilometers. A large proportion of faint meteors show a sudden increase in brightness at the beginning of the trail. This increase is caused by the crumbling of the meteoroid when it first encounters atmospheric resistance. The "breakup" pressure is surprisingly small, 2×10^4 dynes cm^{-2}. This pressure is about $\frac{1}{50}$ of the normal atmospheric pressure, showing that the fragments in the meteoroid are only loosely held. These and other facts have led to the concept of a dustball, and this concept is consistent with our knowledge of comets, the place of origin of meteoroids.

It is of interest to restate the basic equations of the meteor process on the hypothesis that the meteoroid is a dustball which disintegrates into a large number of fragments. If the meteoroid breaks up into n identical fragments, the mass of each fragment is m/n. If the meteoroid of radius r breaks up into m spherical fragments, then the radius of each fragment is $rn^{-1/3}$. Instead of Equation (2.2), the drag equation becomes

$$\frac{dv}{dt} = \frac{3\Gamma\rho v^2}{4r\delta} n^{1/3} \tag{2.7}$$

Under the assumption of total fragmentation the deceleration will thus be expected to increase by the cube root of the number of fragments. If the dustball contains 10^6 fragments, the deceleration will be 10^2 times as great as that which has been predicted by the classical theory.

The rate of loss of mass has to be derived by adding together the mass loss from each individual fragment. For the ith fragment, Equation (2.3) becomes

$$\zeta \left(\frac{dm}{dt}\right)_i = \tfrac{1}{2}\Lambda\pi r_i^2 \rho v_i^3 \tag{2.8}$$

If the meteoroid breaks into n identical spherical fragments, the total mass loss becomes

$$\zeta \frac{dm}{dt} = \tfrac{1}{2} \Lambda\pi r^2 \rho v^2 n^{1/3} \tag{2.9}$$

The rate of loss of mass has been increased by the cube root of the number of fragments when compared with the single-body theory.

These equations show that the breakup of a dustball causes it to decelerate more rapidly than it would if it remained a single body. It also evaporates more rapidly after fragmentation. These two facts help to explain the results in Figure 2.2, where the trails are shorter than the single-body theory would predict. Furthermore, the simple light curve given by Equation (2.6) does not apply to the individual fragments. Equation (2.6) assumes that the meteoroid has been injected into the top of the atmosphere, whereas the fragments have usually been released at some lower height.

Fragmentation during ablation has a considerable effect on the brightness of the meteor. For example, breakup into a million fragments produces a hundredfold increase in the brightness of the meteor. From Equation (1.1) we can see that this corresponds to an increased brightness of 5 magnitude, which is considerable. The degree of fragmentation is not known with accuracy at the present time; however, if $n = 10^6$, a meteor with a magnitude of $+3$ is visible to the unaided eye only because of its crumbling in the atmosphere. Without the process of fragmentation its magnitude would have been $+8$, and good binoculars would have been required to see it.

On the other hand, when prefragmentation occurs, neither the brightness nor the shape of the light curve is affected. If the meteoroid is a cluster of independent particles when it enters the atmosphere, then each particle will, to the first approximation, follow the classical theory. The mass of each particle will be m/n, and the light curve of each particle will be given by Equation (2.6). When the luminosities of the m particles are added together, the value of $I_{\max}$ will be the same as the value for a single particle of mass m.

The apparent paradox that the fragments can either produce an increase in brightness or behave as a single body is explained by a detail of the theory that has so far been ignored. If the intensity is derived from Equations (2.3) and (2.4), it can be shown that the air density at maximum light depends upon the radius, $\rho_{max} \sim r$. Thus, independent fragments entering the top of the atmosphere produce their trail at a higher altitude than they would if the cluster were held together. In Equation (2.9) the density becomes $\rho/n^{1/3}$, and it can be seen that the mass loss is identical to that of a single body but the height of the trail is anomalously high.

Fragmentation need not necessarily occur at one instant. A process of continual fragmentation has been detected in the brighter visual meteors. Under these conditions, the meteoroid sheds fragments continually as it penetrates the atmosphere, sometimes exploding at the end of the trail to produce a flare; the equations will then be a combination of the effects of the single-body meteoroid and the cluster of fragments that exist at any time.

The maximum brightness of a meteor is dependent on the rate of loss of mass dm/dt, and it is of interest to relate this to the mass m before entering the atmosphere. Then a simple scale can be set up relating magnitude and total mass. It is convenient to start with the classical theory, which applies to a single body with no fragmentation, and then modify the result for fragmentation within the atmosphere. The theory shows that the mass is reduced to 8/27 of the original mass at the point of maximum light. It can be shown that

$$\frac{dm}{dt} = \frac{4}{9}\frac{m}{H} v \cos z \tag{2.10}$$

where H is the scale height of the atmosphere (assumed to be isothermal) and z is the angle between the meteor trail and the vertical. In the meteor zone, $H = 6.5 \times 10^5$ cm, and $I_{max} = 6.84 \times 10^{-7} mv^4 \cos z$. Equation (1.1) becomes

$$M = 24.3 - 2.5 \log_{10} (6.84 \times 10^{-17} mv^4 \cos z) \tag{2.11}$$

Thus a meteoroid with mass 1 g and velocity 3×10^6 cm sec^{-1}, approaching the atmosphere at $z = 45$ deg, will produce a meteor with a brightness at maximum of magnitude +0.3. At a distance of 100 km, a 1-g meteor is therefore comparable with a zero magnitude star such as Vega. At a velocity of 20 km sec^{-1}, the required mass is 2 g, and at 45 km sec^{-1} it is 0.5 g.

According to the classical curve, a zero-magnitude meteor will remain above the visual threshold of +5 over a height range of about 35 km. Consequently the path length would be 35 sec z km. The duration of visibility would be 35 sec z/v seconds, which for a 30-km-sec^{-1} meteor approaching at an angle of 45 deg is 1.6 seconds.

Fragmentation within the atmosphere will reduce the duration and path length and increase the brightness. As an approximate relation it may be assumed that dm/dt will vary inversely with path length. Thus if the path and duration are $1/f$ of the value predicted by the classical theory, the brightness will increase by 2.5 $\log_{10} f$ magnitudes. Again, if we assume that the meteor has broken into fragments close to the point of maximum light, the number of fragments can be deduced from Equation (2.9), $n \simeq f^3$.

The effects of a meteor on the atmosphere are not confined to its narrow trajectory. The vaporized atoms leave the meteoroid with a small velocity that carries the atoms away from the trajectory. The meteor atoms collide with the air, and further scattering is produced. The process of fragmentation itself also contributes to the width of the meteor trail, no matter how gently these fragments are dislodged. An intense amount of thermal energy is released along the track, with a consequent expansion of the column of gases. As electrons are released, they diffuse into the upper atmosphere with a speed that is a function of temperature. All these processes tend to enlarge the region of interaction and give a finite thickness to the meteor trail. For an average visual meteor with a magnitude of +3, the trail is approximately 1 m in diameter. Under abnormal conditions, such as explosive fragmentation, the trail can be considerably wider.

The excited atoms in the meteor trail emit radiation that enables us to study the chemical composition of the meteoroid. Spectral analysis shows many bright emission lines from the excited vapor, and on very rare occasions radiation from the hot surface of the meteoroid has been detected. The emission lines reveal the presence of iron, sodium, and magnesium. Calcium, silicon, aluminum, and manganese have also been detected. These elements are the ones that would be expected to appear if meteors had a composition similar to that of the asteroids or the Earth. The chemical abundance of the solid matter in the solar system is predominantly made up of silicon, a fact that explains its presence in the emission spectra. Oxygen and nitrogen will also be expected in meteoroids, but the emission lines from these elements are not located in the visible spectrum and therefore cannot readily be observed. One bright meteor has shown the emission lines of molecular nitrogen, N_2, but in this case the emission was thought to come from the molecular nitrogen in the upper atmosphere rather than from the meteoroid itself.

Some of the lines are from excited ions; that is to say, the atom from the meteor has become ionized, and the positive ion has itself been raised to an excited state. Notable among the ionized lines are the Fraunhofer H and K lines of calcium and the lines of singly ionized iron, silicon, and strontium.

There is a general tendency for excitation and ionization to build up as the meteor penetrates the atmosphere. Sometimes a fast meteor reveals this change to the naked eye, when the color shows a decided shift from a red to a bluish tinge as the meteor approaches the end of its path. The reason for this progressive change is not well understood; it has been suggested that the changes are due to the buildup of a thick vapor cap around the meteoroid, but further work is required to check this suggestion.

A small proportion of the brighter meteors show a spectrum of iron and nickel. Of some 300 spectra, not more than half a dozen meteors have shown this total lack of stony material. These meteors are presumed to be iron meteorites that have been consumed in the atmosphere without landing on the surface of the Earth. None of these irons have appeared as members of the meteor streams. They are regarded as fragments of asteroids and in every way seem to be quite distinct from the average cometary meteoroid.

When a meteor has a negative magnitude, that is to say, when it is brighter than zero magnitude, it sometimes produces a persistent glow in the sky. This column of light is termed a *persistent train*. There is more chance of a train occurring when the meteor has a high velocity and when its magnitude is very great. In fact, there is a rough proportionality between the duration of a train and the brightness of the meteor. On rare occasions observers have been able to study a meteor train with binoculars or a telescope. Observations show that it is much wider than the original trail of the meteor. Sometimes a meteor train expands to a diameter of 1 km. Occasionally the train shows a faint dark line along its axis, as though the glowing column of light has become hollow. As the train expands, the source of energy at the center becomes depleted and the light fades. On one occasion a bright Leonid meteor was seen to leave a train which lasted for 3 hours and was watched by British and French observers as it was carried by winds across the English Channel.

Only one spectrum has yet been obtained of an enduring meteor train, and the emission lines were produced by neutral atoms. The source of energy which sustains the light is not known. Some astronomers have suggested that the light is caused by the recombination of positive ions and electrons, but this has been shown to be an inadequate source of energy. The train seems to contain particles with stored energy which is released at a very slow rate as the particles interact with the atmosphere.

The effects produced by a meteor gradually disappear. It probably takes several hours for the atmosphere to return to its original condition. The positive ions recombine with the electrons, becoming neutral atoms once again. Thus atoms of the meteoroid are dispersed in the upper atmosphere and gradually mix in with the other constituents. The thermal shock is carried into an ever-increasing volume of the upper atmosphere and becomes dissipated. The excited atoms and ions return to the ground state with the emission of the appropriate photons.

✳ 3 ✳

methods
of
observation

The visual observer is becoming obsolete. The meteor appears unexpectedly, moving for a fraction of a second against the background of the stars, and during this instant of surprise the observer has to make subjective estimates of position, rate of movement, and brightness. Although he may use various aids to determine the track, such as a stretched string that he aligns with the meteor, or overhead grids, he can never hope to compete with a camera. Furthermore, the camera gives a permanent record that can be checked in case of doubt, whereas the meteor observer depends entirely on his impressions during the brief instant of the meteor's appearance.

The first systematic photography of meteors was carried out by W. L. Elkin over a period of 16 years from 1893 to 1909. The class of camera that he used has become known as a "small camera," the type used in portrait or landscape photography, with a lens of some 20 cm in focal length and an aperture of about 5 cm. In conventional photography the speed of a camera is measured by the "f-number" and is numerically equal to f/A, where A is the diameter of the aperture of the lens and f is the focal length. The amount of light collected from a scene is proportional to A^2. This light is spread over the image area, which is proportional to f^2. Thus (f-number)$^{-2}$ is proportional to the amount of light falling on the film, and the relative sensitivity of two cameras is proportional to the ratio of their $(A/f)^2$ values.

The speed of a camera in meteor photography cannot be estimated from the f-number alone. A meteor, like a star, is recorded as a round spot as it moves across the film. For fast speeds, coarse-grain film is used, and the theoretical resolving power of the camera lens is not achieved in practice; the image size is controlled by the grain of emulsion. The light collected by lenses of various sizes is concentrated into an area of constant size on the film, and the brightness of the image is proportional to A^2. Now the meteor is moving across the field so that the linear speed across the film is proportional to f, so the duration of exposure varies as $1/f$ and the sensitivity of the camera varies as A^2/f. In meteor photography, of course, the linear size of the aperture is important as well as the f-number; a miniature camera with a small f-number will not produce good results.

The extreme limiting visual magnitude M of a camera of aperture A cm and focal length f can be written

$$M = 2.5 \log_{10} A^2/f \qquad \text{(3.1)}$$

It is presumed that the camera is loaded with a fast film, such as Tri-X. This relationship holds for slow meteors or meteors with appreciable foreshortening near the radiant. Under average conditions the limiting magnitude will be about one magnitude brighter, or $M_{av} = M - 1$. From Equation (3.1) and the known influx rate of meteors, an approximate expression can be derived for the hourly rate N of photographed meteors for any particular camera:

$$N = 4 \times 10^{-6} \, w^2 \, A^{2.7} \, f^{-1.3} \qquad \text{(3.2)}$$

where w is the width of the field of view in degrees. The expected hourly rate for various types of cameras is given in Table 3.1. These values apply to sporadic meteors. During the progress of a major meteor shower the number will be higher by a factor of roughly 10.

TABLE 3.1   EXPECTED HOURLY RATE N FOR VARIOUS CAMERAS

	f-number	f, cm	A, cm	w, deg	M	N, hr^{-1}
Small camera	4	20	5	45	0.2	1×10^{-2}
35-mm camera	1.5	4.5	3	45	0.8	2×10^{-2}
Super-Schmidt camera	0.8	20	31	55	4.2	2
200-in. telescope	3.3	1,690	508	$\frac{1}{30}$	5.4	4×10^{-6}

With modern film, a small camera of the type used by Elkin is able to photograph meteors of magnitude 0 and brighter. With a field of view of some 45 deg, an observer may expect to photograph 1 meteor during every 100 hours of exposure. This is a very small yield for the efforts involved. With the plates available in 1900, the rate of successful photographs was even lower, and Elkin's work did nothing more than establish the feasibility of the two-camera technique. It was many years before the work of Elkin was repeated.

During the period from 1936 to 1942, F. L. Whipple carried out a small-camera program with observing sites set 37 km apart in Massachusetts. Each camera was provided with a rotating shutter driven by a synchronous electric motor, and the image of the meteor was interrupted many times during its movement across the sky. Instead of a continuous streak being produced on the photographic plate, a dashed line was obtained. From the spacing of the dashes the duration and hence the speed of the meteor could be accurately determined. (Each camera was set on an axis that pointed toward the North Celestial Pole and rotated about this axis to follow the stars in their diurnal motion. Thus the background of stars showed as individual points which could be used for fixing the path of the meteor.) The double-station technique gave the heights of every portion of the trail, as well as the radiant point. In addition, the measurements were accurate enough to show for the first time the deceleration of the meteoroid as it encountered the resistance of the air.

After 8 years of intensive effort the meteor patrol produced double-station photographs of some 52 meteors. These hard-earned results were extremely useful in the study of meteor streams and in the preliminary estimates of upper-air density. In 1948 the small cameras were transferred from Massachusetts to the White Sands Desert in New Mexico. Largely as a result of the improved atmospheric conditions the yield increased to approximately 2 meteors for every 100 hours of observation. This increase in sensitivity added many more meteors to the lists. Further results have been obtained by Russian, Czechoslovakian, and Japanese astronomers using small cameras.

A standard 35-mm slide camera will photograph approximately twice as many meteors as the small camera. As Table 3.1 shows, an f-1.5 camera with Tri-X film will yield approximately 1 meteor trail for every 50 hours of photography. (Because of the increase in numbers of meteors with fainter magnitudes, the majority of trails on the film are faint and close to the photographic limit.) Even more time must be spent in exposure if a photograph of a bright meteor is required. During a shower such as that of the Perseids, the rate of photography may be as high as one trail per night. To overcome these fearful odds, meteor observers sometimes use five or six cameras simultaneously to cover the entire sky, thus guaranteeing at least one or two successful exposures per night.

A fast 35-mm camera will photograph more meteors than a small camera, but the small size of the negative is a disadvantage. The coarseness of the grain shows up with only a small amount of magnification, and precise measurements of the trail are difficult to make. Because of this limitation 35-mm cameras have not been used to any great extent for precise photographic work. They have been used in correlation work with radar equipment where an approximate record is needed of the track of a meteor across the sky. The magnitude of the meteor can be estimated from the films of small cameras and 35-mm cameras with almost equal accuracy. P. M. Millman used a set of 35-mm cameras during the Giacobinid meteor storm on October 10, 1946. He was planning to make his observations from the Dominion Observatory, Ottawa, but the weather was unfavorable. The cluster of 35-mm cameras had the big advantage of being portable, and during the critical hours of the meteor storm the equipment was flown by a Canadian Air Force plane to North Bay. Successful photographs were made of 204 of these remarkable meteors—photographs which could not have been obtained with fixed cameras at the home observatory. The all-time record goes to L. A. Manning of Stanford, California, who photographed 17 meteor trails during a 1-minute exposure at the peak of the Giacobinid storm. The expected rate for his camera is 2×10^{-2} trails hr^{-1} when the visual rate has its average value of 10 hr^{-1}. A simple scaling shows that his result corresponds to a visual rate of 500,000 meteors hr^{-1}, truly a staggering figure.

The *pièce de résistance* in meteor photography is the Super-Schmidt camera designed by James G. Baker. This camera was designed especially for meteor photography and, quite naturally, out-performs any other instrument. The limiting visual magnitude of the Super-Schmidt is +4, and the field of view is 55 deg in diameter. Athough the 200-in. reflecting telescope on Mount Palomar would theoretically have a limiting magnitude fainter than the Super-Schmidt, the field of view is so small that almost a million hours of photography would be required to yield a photographic trail. Because of its wide field of view and large aperture the

Super-Schmidt photographs 100 times as many meteors per exposure hour as does a 35-mm camera. The bulk of our knowledge of meteors brighter than magnitude +4 has come from the Super-Schmidt films.

A German optician, Bernhard Schmidt, designed the camera that bears his name. The image in this camera was formed by a spherical silvered mirror instead of a lens. Unless special precautions were taken, the spherical mirror would produce an image badly distorted by spherical aberration. Schmidt overcame this distortion by inserting a glass correcting plate in front of the mirror. With this camera, faint stars could be photographed over a field of view of 10 deg. The original Schmidt was designed to operate at an f-number of approximately 3. Dr. Baker's modification was to decrease the f-number considerably (and enlarge the field of view). In fact the Super-Schmidt has gone to the extreme limit possible with conventional techniques and materials.

The revolutionary design is shown in Figure 3.1. The correcting plate has been modified by the addition of two large hemispherical glass lenses. These are placed in front of the spherical mirror, which is approximately 2 ft in diameter. The optics are so extreme that the photographic film is required to rest above one of the hemispherical glass shells. It may be said that in this camera the photographic film is placed *within* the lens system. As a further complication, the image produced by the mirror is curved, and it is necessary to curve the film in order to follow the focal plane. When the camera was first designed, many scientists shook their heads with pessimism. Curving film to this extent had never been done before, and how could a camera be trusted when the lens components had to be taken apart each time a new film was inserted? Nevertheless these problems were solved. Flat sheet film was heated and molded to the approximate spherical shape. The film was held accurately within the focal plane by suction. A metal plate of the desired shape was fixed between the correcting lenses, and air was continually pumped from the narrow space between the film and the plate so as to hold the two together. The lens components were separated by a robust, precisely engineered hinge and were pressed down onto a metallic seat when the camera was closed.

The rotating shutter caused a further engineering problem. It would have been inelegant and perhaps impossible to mount the

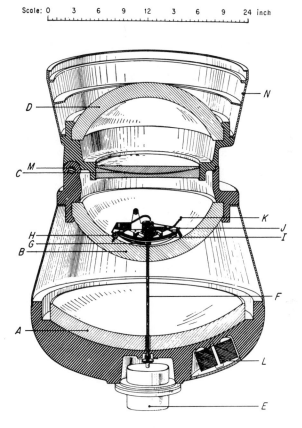

Scale: 0   3   6   9   12   3   6   9   24 inch

FIGURE 3.1   Cross-sectional view of Super-Schmidt camera. (A) Main mirror; (B) rear glass shell; (C) correcting plate; (D) front glass shell; (E) shutter motor; (F) shutter shaft; (G) rotating shutter; (H) focusing post; (I) film holder; (J) film-holder hinge; (K) vacuum line; (L) counter weight; (M) hinge for opening camera; (N) dew cap. *Courtesy Dominion Observatory.*

rotating shutter in front of the lens system. In this position the shutter would have been over 4 ft in diameter and rotating at several hundred revolutions per minute. A hole was drilled through the primary spherical mirror and through one of the correcting glass shells. A rotating shaft was then placed along the optic axis of the system, and the shutter was located immediately in front of the film. With this idea the shutter was required to be only 8 in. in diameter instead of 4 ft, though the blades had to be curved to match the film. The long shaft was not entirely free of trouble, since there was a tendency for it to whip and vibrate as it was spinning. The occultations of the meteor did not occur at an exactly constant rate, and the accuracy of the measurements was impaired. This problem soon became known as "shutter flutter," and it was essential to find a cure for it. Similar cameras were made in Britain, where the problem was solved by using jets of air to drive the rotating shutter. In this way no spindle was required, and no vibration of the shutter occurred. In the American model the problem was solved by enlarging the driving spindle and the bearings in which it rotated.

A meteor photograph is measured by reading off the x and y values of each point of the meteor trail and of nearby star images. The two coordinates may be measured with an error of no more than a few microns, using a traveling microscope with accurate screws for the two coordinates. However, the curved film of the Super-Schmidt cameras could not be measured by the conventional method. It was necessary to design a special copying camera that converted the image on the spherical film to an image on a flat plate.

Four Super-Schmidt cameras are used in the meteor program at Harvard College Observatory. Two cameras were originally set up at Doña Ana and Soledad in the Desert of New Mexico. Although the skies were clear, the conditions in the desert were primitive; the roads were treacherous, and the cameras were endangered by the intense heat of noon and the wind-blown dust. The two cameras were therefore relocated in the cooler and more conveniently accessible peaks of the Sacramento mountain range. The number of cameras was increased to four when two extra cameras were set up for the special purpose of photographing meteor trains. These cameras were maintained at the ready and were fired by the observer when a bright meteor appeared in the field of view. When the firing program was actuated, the cameras swung through an angle of about 1 deg in successive stages, so that several images of the meteor train were obtained during its lifetime. This technique necessarily placed the camera operator under the same type of strain as a visual observer. He was required to keep alert through the night, since it was essential to fire the cameras within about half a second of the appearance of a bright meteor. Yet there was seldom more than one suitable meteor during any particular night, and on many occasions the observer fired the camera only to find that the meteor did not produce a worthwhile train.

Two Super-Schmidt cameras have been set up in northern Alberta, Canada, by the Dominion Observatory. These cameras are almost identical to the Harvard Super-Schmidt; in fact they were made by the same optical corporation. The northern observing site was chosen to fill in our information on meteors at high latitudes. Particular interest lay in possible differences in the height of meteors, which in turn would indicate a difference in the height of the atmosphere. Three Super-Schmidt cameras have also been built at the University of Bristol, England. Two of them were almost identical to the original Super-Schmidt, though some slight improvements in design were possible on the basis of experience gained with the first models. In particular, the field of view was enlarged by 1 degree, and the effective f-number was reduced by 5 per cent. The third English camera was built on a scale of two-thirds of the original model. At first sight this might be regarded as a backward step, since it would undoubtedly decrease the sensitivity of the camera by at least one-half a magnitude; however, by scaling down the camera there was a considerable saving in cost, and the problems of shaping the mirror and lenses were considerably reduced. One of the British cameras is set up in North Wales, where meteors are photographed simultaneously with radar observations.

In principle it is simple to obtain the spectrum of a meteor. With the conventional spectroscope, the operator has to focus the light from a star onto a narrow slit and then photograph the slit through a prism. A meteor trail is a very narrow line in the sky and therefore provides its own slit image. If a prism with a 30-deg angle is placed in front of the camera lens a separate image of the meteor is produced for every color that is present. A diffraction grating placed in front of the camera lens will produce the same results. A diffraction grating is more useful than a prism because the direct image of the meteor is photographed as well. The particular colors present in the light of the meteor are reinforced at definite angles on passage through the grating, and the position of the meteor spectral lines can be measured with reference to the direct image.

In practice there are difficulties. The meteor must travel parallel to the angle of the prism or to the lines of the diffraction grating if the spectral lines are to stand upright. If the meteor is tilted, the spectral lines are also tilted. If the meteor moves perpendicular to the angle of the prism, the images of the different colors are superimposed, and no spectrum is obtained.

The absorption in the glass and the scattering in the grating reduce the quantity of light available from the meteor. In addition, the very act of dispersing the light into the various colored components reduces the intensity of the image. The sensitivity of a camera is usually about two magnitudes fainter when it is used for spectrographic work. The expected rate of photography is therefore about one-tenth of the rate given in Table 3.1. The rates for small cameras and 35-mm cameras are very low indeed. Even for a Super-Schmidt, more than one meteor spectrum per night of observation could not be expected. In the case of the Super-Schmidts, the technical problems for spectral photography have not been solved at the time of writing. It is not possible to produce a uniform ruled grating to cover the 2-ft aperture of the camera, nor is it possible to mold a uniform prism of this size.

It is not practical to use the conventional telescopes in observatories for meteor photography because of the low rate of detection. Occasionally a meteor trail is photographed by chance as it crosses the field of view during a long exposure of a faint galaxy or star field. Many trails were obtained during the photographic survey of the sky carried out with the 48-in. Schmidt telescope on Mount Palomar. This telescope has a remarkable resolving power. Theoretically two objects 6 in. apart at a distance of 100 km would be separated by this instrument. Of course turbulence in the atmosphere disturbs the image to some extent, and the resolving power at a distance of 100 km is about ½ m. A special program was undertaken with this instrument to determine the width of meteor trails. The telescope is normally focused on the stars at infinity, and in this series of measurements a small adjustment was made to focus on the meteors so as to obtain maximum resolving power. By pointing the telescope at the radiant of the Geminid meteor stream, the meteor trails were considerably foreshortened. In this way meteors were photographed some two or three magnitudes below the normal limit. One trail photographed in this way had a visual magnitude of +9.

The radar technique is now becoming more important than photography in the study of meteors. Radar measurements can be made during daylight hours and during periods of cloud and moonlight when the camera is inoperative. Modern technology permits a radar system to detect meteors much fainter than the limit of the Super-Schmidt camera. The position and speed of meteors of magnitude +10 have been measured with a high degree of accuracy—more than 100 times fainter than the limit of the camera—and echoes can be detected from meteors as faint as magnitude +15. The radar system can be made to operate automatically and the powerful methods of modern electronics brought to bear on the problem. For example, the signals returned from a meteor trail can be recorded as a series of numbers on magnetic tape, the tape can be fed directly to a digital computing machine, all the complex calculations can be made in less than a second, and the finished results can be printed out in a concise form ready for the radar astronomer to use.

Radar, developed in World War II for the detection of aircraft and ships, has become an indispensable aid to traffic control, navigation, and basic research. A transmitter generates pulses of radio energy. The duration of a pulse is usually short, a few microseconds (10^{-6} sec) for an airport radar, though for specialized studies, such as echoes from the planets or the sun, the pulse can be several seconds in length. The wavelength of the transmitter is set within the centimeter and meter bands, depending on the purpose of the radar. Power is sent out from a reflecting paraboloid antenna or a group of dipoles. The pulses of radio energy are reflected from a target and are returned to the radar site after a certain time delay. The echo is picked up by a receiving antenna and fed by cable or wave guide to the receiver. After suitable amplification, the echo can be displayed on a cathode-ray tube together with the original pulse. The separation of transmitter pulse and echo is proportional to the range of the target. In an airport radar, the base line of the cathode-ray tube sweeps round like the hand of a clock, keeping in synchronism with the rotating antenna. In this manner a two-dimensional range-azimuth map is presented on the display tube, and the position of each airplane is under continuous surveillance.

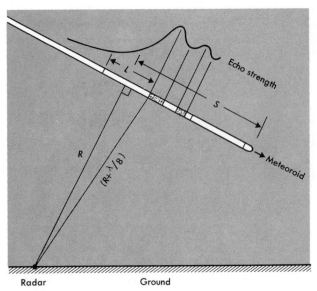

FIGURE 3.2   The formation of Fresnel zones along a meteor trail.

In a meteor radar the transmitter is used to send out pulses of radio energy toward a target at range R. A transmitting antenna is used to increase the power directed toward the target by a factor G, the gain of the antenna over an isotropic radiator. If the peak power of the transmitter is P, the intensity at the target is $PG/4\pi R^2$ watts m^{-2}. The scattering cross section of the target is σ, and all energy falling on this area is scattered in every direction. The power returned to the radar site is therefore $PG\,\sigma/(4\pi R^2)^2$.

If the transmitting antenna is now used to receive the echo, the collecting area of the antenna will be $G \lambda/4\pi$, where λ is the wavelength of the radar. The optimum wavelength for meteor radars is between 5 and 12 m. Now the scattering cross section of a meteor trail depends upon the number of electrons present. The maximum echo power is returned when the meteor trail is perpendicular to the antenna beam, as shown in Figure 3.2, and then a certain length L of the trail provides most of the signal. Because of the path difference δR the signals reflected from various parts of the trail will differ in phase. When $\delta R = \lambda/8$, the reflected signal will be out of phase by $\lambda/4$, or 90 deg. The effective length of the trail is L where $\delta R \lesssim \lambda/8$, and from the triangle in Figure 3.2 it can be shown that $L = \sqrt{\lambda R/2}$. In the length L there will be Lq electrons, since the line density of electrons is q. All electrons will scatter in phase so that the amplitudes add together. Thus the total scattering cross section of the meteor is $L^2 q^2 \sigma_e$, where σ_e is the power scattering cross section of an individual electron. Because the electrons are scattering as dipoles with the current perpendicular to the line of sight, the scattering cross section is 1.5 times greater than the classical value, and $\sigma_e = 9.8 \times 10^{-29}$ m². Putting all these terms together, one can derive the power p received in an echo pulse:

$$p = \frac{PG^2\lambda^3 q^2}{128 \pi^3 R^3} \sigma_e \tag{3.3}$$

Equation (3.3) gives the echo power to be expected from a long trail after it has formed. But meteor trails do not form instantaneously. If the meteor at any instant has moved a distance S beyond the minimum range point, the echo power can be written

$$p_x = \frac{p}{2} \left[\int_{-\infty}^{S} \cos \frac{\pi x^2}{2} \, dx \right]^2 + \frac{p}{2} \left[\int_{-\infty}^{S} \sin \frac{\pi x^2}{2} \, dx \right]^2 \tag{3.4}$$

where $x = 2S(R\lambda)^{-\frac{1}{2}}$. This equation results from an integration of the phase and amplitude of all signals returned from the various elements of the trail. It is similar to the equation derived for the intensity of light across the shadow of a straight edge. The integrals are known in optics as *Fresnel integrals,* and the variation of the amplitude of a meteor echo with time is known as a *Fresnel pattern.*

Maxima and minima of echo strength are produced as x increases. The meteor adds reflecting zones to the trail that are alternately in phase and out of phase with the main signal. Figure 3.2 makes it easier to visualize the process. Zones that are in phase with the main signal are shown clear, and zones that are out of phase are shown black. The curve shows the resultant signal strength as it varies with the motion of the meteor. Sometimes a continuous wave (cw) is sent out from a radar transmitter, instead of pulses. Then the Fresnel pattern shows as an audio modulation on the carrier wave.

If the receiving station is not located near the transmitter, radio reflections can still be obtained. The radio pulse is transmitted toward the meteor trail and is reflected as in a mirror toward the Earth's surface. The process is called *forward scatter* and provides a useful way of studying meteors. This method has also been applied successfully in radio communications, since the meteor can furnish a reflecting surface which acts momentarily like the ionosphere.

The unique reflection properties summarized in Equation (3.4) are responsible for the rapid strides made in radar studies of meteors. First, the echo power is vanishingly small if x does not pass through the value zero. That is to say, the meteor trail glints like a mirror and gives a specular reflection if it is perpendicular to the antenna beam. Since the specular point on the trail must be 90 deg away from the radiant, this simple property has been the basis of all radiant determination. Second, the spacing of the zones, and hence the shape of the pattern, is governed entirely by the geometry of Figure 3.2. A fast meteor shows a Fresnel pattern similar in shape to that of a slow meteor, but the slow meteor echo is stretched in time. The time duration between successive maxima gives a measure of the velocity of the meteoroid.

Radiant points have been determined on a routine basis in England and Australia using a single-station radar. A narrow-beam antenna is set up with the beam pointing as nearly as possible toward the horizon. Echoes are recorded one by one as they appear in the antenna beam. When a large number of echoes appear, this indicates a group of meteors moving in parallel paths with a radiant somewhere on the great circle which passes around the sky 90 deg from the antenna beam. To confirm the radiant, observations are also made with a second narrow-beam antenna pointing in a different direction. Usually the antennas differ in azimuth by about

30 deg. As the Earth rotates, antenna 2 swings perpendicular to
the meteor trails, and echoes are detected by it some 2 hours later
than by antenna 1. The transfer of activity from one antenna to
the other confirms the existence of the stream. The mid-time of the
occurrence of the two sets of echoes gives the right ascension of the
radiant point, and the time difference gives the declination of
the radiant. A radiant directly overhead in the zenith would produce echoes simultaneously in antennas 1 and 2, whereas radiants
at some distance from the zenith would produce an appreciable
time difference.

Additional information is given by the range of the echoes and
the manner in which the range changes from echo to echo. A minimum of 10 echoes is needed in each antenna to fix the position of
a stream radiant. The method has therefore been used primarily
for studies of the major streams such as the Perseids and Geminids.
Routine observations have been made almost continuously since the
two-antenna system was developed in 1949. Radar astronomers
engaged in this work appreciate the full meaning of "24 hours per
day, 365¼ days per year," especially since important streams tend
to occur at vacation dates, New Year's, Christmas, and summer.
A check has been kept on the nighttime streams already known to
astronomers, and the daytime streams, invisible to the eye, have
been observed with the same thoroughness.

I have adapted the method to make a statistical study of sporadic
meteors. These meteors do not follow parallel paths, hence the
radiant points are scattered over an area of the sky. They form an
important component of the solar system, since less than 20 per cent
of all meteors belong to the major streams.

By measuring the Fresnel pattern and the range, the velocity of
a meteor can be found, even though its exact position in the atmosphere is not known. Extensive programs have been carried out for
the measurement of the velocity of stream meteors. All the major
streams, daytime and nighttime, have been measured. The accuracy
of an individual measurement of velocity is ± 1 km sec^{-1} for the
bulk of published data. Refinements in our knowledge of the theory
of the Fresnel pattern have decreased the error to $\pm\frac{1}{2}$ km sec^{-1}.
Although still greater accuracy for stream meteors might be ex-

pected by taking average values of a number of observations, this increase is not achieved in practice because of the finite spread in values among members of a stream and because of the uncertainty in the correction for deceleration in the atmosphere.

Velocity surveys have been carried out on sporadic meteors by several observatories with single-station radars. About 11,000 velocities were measured at Ottawa, Canada, between 1948 and 1950. Several thousand have been measured at Manchester, England; Adelaide, Australia; Christchurch, New Zealand; and Stanford, California. The English observers recorded the Fresnel pattern as a series of pulses; the other groups used the continuous-wave method, where the pattern was recorded as a smooth curve. No significant difference has been found between the two techniques.

When cameras are used, two sites are needed to find the height of a meteor. A radar system can fix the height using a single station only. The range of a trail is measured from the time delay of the echo, and if the angle of elevation α of the meteor can also be measured, the height is given by simple trigonometry as $R \tan \alpha$. When α is less than 50 deg, it is necessary to apply an additional correction to allow for the curvature of the Earth's surface. Sometimes the beam width of the antenna is small ($\sim$1 deg), in which case α may be taken as the angle of elevation of the antenna beam. Usually in meteor work the beam width is greater than 10 deg, and other refinements have to be added to measure the angle of elevation.

The angle of elevation can be measured with an error of less than ½ deg by the phase-comparison method. The wave reflected from the meteor returns to the radar and is picked up on two antennas about one wavelength apart. Because of the angle of approach, the wave arrives at one antenna a fraction of a microsecond before it reaches the other. There is a phase difference between the signals from the two antennas, and α is a simple function of this phase difference. If the radar system uses pulses, the phase difference is measured during the very short interval as each pulse returns; if it sends out continuous waves, the phase difference is more easily measured. Despite the electronic differences, the pulse and continuous-wave methods are comparable in the accuracy of the final determination of α.

The *pièce de résistance* among radars is the multistation system. T. R. Kaiser first suggested the refined method of using three or more spaced stations with a transmitter at one site as shown in Figure 3.3. The home station has the transmitter with all the recording instruments. The slave stations receive a skip reflection from the meteor trail, and the pulses are carried by radio links back to the home station. Each station produces a Fresnel pattern, and

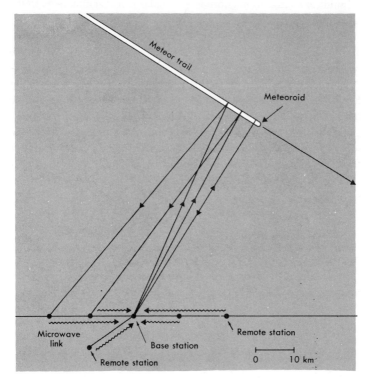

FIGURE 3.3   The geometry of a multistation meteor radar.

when the meteor passes by, its velocity can be measured with precision. In addition there is a time delay between the echoes at each station due to the separation of the reflecting points on the trail. The time delays depend upon the angle of approach of the meteor, and so its direction and radiant can be found. By providing a phase measurement at one site to give the angle of elevation, the height of the trail can be determined. Deceleration of the meteoroid can be obtained by noting the decrease in velocity as the meteor passes from one station to the next, and the variation of electron density, or light curve, can be followed. Thus the multistation radar does all that a Super-Schmidt pair can do. Whereas the Super-Schmidt is limited to magnitude $+4$, radar can reach meteors much fainter at $+12$ or $+15$.

The first three-station system was set up at Manchester, England, and the second at Adelaide, South Australia. The English prototype was a pulse radar, the Australian was continuous-wave. A three-station radar has been set up in Kharkov, Russia, which is similar to the English pulsed system. A six-station system is in operation in the United States at Havana, Illinois, jointly operated by Harvard College Observatory and the Smithsonian Astrophysical Observatory. Figure 3.4 shows a sample record with the Fresnel patterns from six stations recorded together on a film. The time delay between the various channels is apparent.

※ **4** ※

**swarms
and
streams**

The most spectacular events in meteor astronomy are, unfortunately, very rare. A meteor storm occurs not more than three or four times each century, and even then the peak of the activity is confined to a time span of no more than an hour. The chance of seeing a meteor storm on taking a casual look at the night sky is not much better than one in a million. The occurrence of a swarm can never be predicted with certainty, and astronomers have been caught almost unawares by several of the storms during the last century. Only one storm in the history of meteor astronomy has been studied by modern observing methods, with camera and radar, and even then only single-station measurements were carried out. For the bulk of our information we have to rely on visual observations and eye-witness accounts.

The Leonid storm produced a dramatic display of shooting stars in 1799, 1833, and 1866. Very little has been seen of Leonid meteors since 1866. By studying historical records some evidence has been produced to show that the Leonids may have occurred previously as early as 585 A.D., but the evidence for a dramatic storm is not conclusive. Other swarms have made only two or three returns, and it would not be unreasonable to assume that the Leonid swarm has probably conformed to this pattern. The great explorer, Alexander von Humboldt, reported a meteor storm on the night of November 11, 1799. He saw "thousands of meteors and fireballs moving regularly from north to south with no part of the sky so large as twice the moon's diameter not filled each instant by meteors." The hourly rate can be computed from this description. Assuming the average length of the trail to be 10 deg, each meteor would occupy, according to Humboldt's estimate, 10 deg^2 in the sky. With a field of view of 2,000 deg^2 a visual observer would see 200 meteors at any instant. If the average duration of a meteor was 1 second, the hourly rate would be 7.2×10^5, or close to a million.

On November 12, 1833, the spectacle was repeated. People were taken by surprise, and it is difficult to estimate the hourly rate. Some descriptions talk of "meteors as thick as snowflakes," while other estimates place the rate at 10,000 hr^{-1}. The phenomenon of the radiant point was noticed for the first time in 1833. The meteors were streaming from the sickle in the constellation of Leo, and the radiant point moved with the diurnal motion of the stars. Thus it was inferred that the particles were entering the Earth's atmosphere in parallel paths, and members of the swarm were traveling along the same orbit in space. The great storm reported by Humboldt and earlier displays indicated a period of between 33 and 34 years. A further encounter with the swarm of particles was predicted for the year 1866 and was seen by European and American observers on the night of November 13.

By 1866 the connection of the Leonid swarm with a comet was well established. The political refugee Wilhelm Temple was searching the sky for comets that year in Marseilles. He discovered the faint comet that bears his name, and it was realized simultaneously by many astronomers that the orbit of the comet was the same as the orbit of the Leonid swarm. The orbit of the meteors and the orbit of the comet are given for comparison in Table 4.1.

TABLE 4.1   SWARMS AND COMET ORBITS

SWARM	DATE	PERIOD, yr	a, AU	q, AU	e	ω	Ω	i
Leonids	Nov. 11, 1799 Nov. 12, 1833 Nov. 13, 1866	45.6	12.76	0.970	0.924	173.7	235.0	162.5
Comet Temple		33.2	10.03	0.977	0.905	171.0	231.4	162.7
Andromedids	Nov. 27, 1872 Nov. 27, 1885 Nov. 23, 1892	4.97	2.88	0.785	0.728	245.4	228.1	6.3
Comet Biela		6.3	3.41	0.750	0.780	237.7	230.5	7.5
Giacobinids	Oct. 9, 1933 Oct. 10, 1946	6.59	3.51	0.996	0.717	171.8	196.2	30.7
Comet Giacobini-Zinner		6.59	3.51	0.996	0.717	171.8	196.2	30.7

Some Leonid activity was seen in 1867 and in the following years, but no great storm occurred at the predicted return in 1899. The reason for the failure was the planet Jupiter. On its way to the sun the swarm passed by Jupiter in 1898, and the gravitational field of the planet deflected the particles away from the Earth by 2×10^6 km. No Leonid storms have been seen since 1866, though one or two stragglers have been picked up by the Super-Schmidt and other photographic patrols, and on some occasions a moderate visual shower has been seen. For example, in 1932 the hourly rate rose to 240, and in 1962 about one hundred were seen, which raised hopes for a good display in 1966. The orbital elements given in Table 4.1 are the average values of the few Leonid meteors that have been accurately measured by the photographic technique. Perhaps sometime in the future a favorable perturbation will occur, and the Leonid swarm will be once more deflected into the path of the Earth.

A small comet was discovered by Montagne in 1772. Because it moved around the sun with a period of 6⅔ years, it was rediscovered on succeeding perihelion passages. Jean Louis Pons saw it in 1805, and von Biela discovered it again in 1826. The comet finally became known as Biela's Comet. In 1845 two comets were seen instead of one, and it was presumed that Comet Biela had split in two. At the next return in 1852 the two comets had separated by approximately 2×10^6 km, and the components were faint. The comet was not seen again after 1852, and astronomers presumed that it had disintegrated.

Perturbations from the planets were operating on the comet and the debris surrounding it. The comet orbit was gradually moved across the orbit of the Earth, and at one stage in the perturbation the cometary orbit was no more than a few thousand miles away from the Earth's orbit. According to calculations made from the elements of the orbit, the closest approach was in 1839 with a separation of only 13,500 km, but this figure cannot be relied on because of the errors inherent in the orbital elements. Nor was the comet seen in 1839, because it reached the Earth's orbit some 6 months ahead of the Earth and was hidden from view by the glare of the sun. In a way this separation in time was fortunate, for within the limits of error astronomers were predicting a direct hit. Comet hunters would have had a grandstand view of Biela, but the Earth would have developed a gaping crater some 10 or 20 miles across, with devastation spread over hundreds of square miles.

It is difficult to say exactly when the first meteors from Biela's Comet were seen. Brandes, one of the pioneering meteor observers, reported a shower in early December, 1798, with a rate of 400 hr^{-1}. Careful reading of his account shows that there is some doubt about the rate, because he saw the meteors while riding on top of a mail coach and applied a correction factor to allow for obscuration by trees, etc. By 1867 a weak stream was known to occur around November 29 or 30 with a radiant in the constellation of Andromeda. At this time, spurred by the identification of Temple's Comet as the cause of the Leonids, several astronomers pointed out that Biela's Comet might well be the cause of the Andromedids, even though the comet had disintegrated. But nobody expected the great meteor storm of 1872, not from a defunct comet.

In the early evening of November 27, 1872, European observers saw the sky filled with meteors moving from the radiant in the Andromeda. The duration of the storm and the maximum rate are not known with certainty because of the near-impossibility of making reliable measurements when caught unawares. The duration of the storm seems to have been about 1 hour and the peak rate 3,000 hr^{-1}. However, a rate of about 100 min^{-1} is about the maximum rate of counting that an unprepared observer can manage. Without special restrictions to the field of view, or without the ingenious method of estimation used by Humboldt, a person is saturated at this rate, and the count must necessarily represent a lower limit.

After a quiet period of 13 years the Earth again collided with the swarm on November 27, 1885. Despite the fact that many people tumbled out of bed to see the show, only sparse information can be gleaned from the accounts. The radiant point was at R.A. $24°5$, Dec. $44°7$, close to the position expected from the old comet orbit. The hourly rate was estimated to lie somewhere between 5,000 and 75,000, but it could easily have been greater. Another display, though somewhat weaker, occurred on November 23, 1892, and by 1905 the Andromedids were considered to be lost. The perturbations from Jupiter and other planets that had moved the swarm into the path of the Earth had finally shifted the debris out of the collision zone.

Today, a few stragglers are found each year on the Super-Schmidt films. From November 2 to 22 the rate obtained by the cameras averages 1 meteor in 10 hours. This would correspond to a rate of 0.3 hr^{-1} for a visual observer, a rate that would hardly be noticed because of the higher rate of sporadic meteors. On November 14 the visual rate rises to 3 hr^{-1}, as estimated from the photographic records. At this level of activity the stream might well be noticed if several hours of observation were undertaken.

The orbits of the stragglers tell the story of the swarm. The old comet orbit, and presumably the orbit of the swarm if it still exists, passes over the North Pole of the Earth on November 3. The separation between the swarm and the Earth is 4×10^6 km, which is too great for a collision to take place. The Andromedids detected by the cameras have been perturbed from the swarm but still remain in the plane of the comet's orbit. A slight difference in velocity among the members of the swarm will over a period of many years disperse the particles in the plane of the original orbit. Dispersion of particles out of the orbital plane does not occur so easily. A small perturbation will cause the particle to oscillate above and below the original plane with no progressive separation. The Earth passes through the plane of the orbit of the swarm on November 14, and on that date the maximum number of Andromedids are seen. It is interesting to note that an amateur astronomer, R. M. Dole, reported a shower on November 15, 1940. The hourly rate reached 30, and the radiant was in the constellation Andromeda. Although no velocity measurements were made and therefore no orbit is available to confirm the identity of the stream, the later photographic work makes it highly probable that Mr. Dole did indeed see a sudden burst of activity from the lost Andromedid swarm.

So far in the present century only two meteor swarms have been seen, and both were produced by the same comet. The comet was discovered by Giacobini in 1900 and rediscovered by Zinner in 1913; it is still intact and making regular visits to the sun. The comet has been deflected slightly by Jupiter on each revolution, and its orbit has almost intersected the orbit of the Earth on several occasions. The closest approach was in the year 1926, but no meteor storm was seen on this occasion. (A few meteors were seen, including a fireball of magnitude -7, but the hourly rate never exceeded 17.) The absence of a storm is not easy to explain. One can make the general statement that not every close encounter with a comet orbit produces a storm and that the meteor debris is not scattered uniformly in the comet orbit, but this is more a statement of the facts than an explanation of the phenomenon. One can never be sure that the Earth will pass through a cloud of debris, and any prediction of a storm is in the nature of a gamble.

In 1933, although the miss distance was somewhat greater

$(7.5 \times 10^5 \text{ km})$, the Earth made contact with a swarm, and visual observers were well repaid for their patience. The meteors struck the Earth at 2000 UT and were therefore visible only to European observers. The proverbial cloud cover was present, handicapping the observations. Most of England was blotted out, but Scotland, Belgium, and Germany were more fortunate. The radiant point was determined and found to agree with the value expected from the comet orbit. The duration of the shower was very short, more than 50 per cent of the meteors being seen during an interval of only 30 minutes. The hourly rate at maximum varied from 5,000 to 19,000, depending on the observer. This variation probably indicates a counting error, since the rate was well beyond the saturation point for a single observer without special equipment. On the other hand, it is possible that local irregularities existed in the swarm and that real differences in influx could occur from one position to another on the Earth's surface. A new and important result was found in the 1933 storm. The number of meteors was counted in each magnitude interval, and it was found that the Giacobinids contained a large proportion of faint meteors. The value of r in Equation (5.3) was found to be 4. This should be contrasted with the value 2.5 for sporadic fireballs and 3.4 for sporadic meteors. The difference indicates that material freshly ejected from a comet contains a higher percentage of fine fragments than the general sporadic complex. If, as is now believed, sporadic meteors represent the end product in the diffusion and perturbation of meteor swarms and streams, some process must be in operation to remove small particles more rapidly from the solar system. The Poynting-Robertson effect is one process that acts on small meteoroids more rapidly than larger bodies. Corpuscular radiation from the sun may also tend to smash meteoroid particles, and the destruction of small particles may be a more rapid process.

In 1939 no contact was made with the swarm, probably because the Earth reached the collision zone some 136 days before the comet. In 1946 a storm was predicted, and the predictions were fulfilled. This return of the Giacobinids is the only storm to be observed by modern methods. It was observed by Millman, using 35-mm cameras equipped with rotating shutters that were taken by a special emergency airlift to North Bay, Canada. Radar observations were made by two groups in England, and simultaneous measurements of the ionosphere were carried out in the United States. Visual observations were carried out on this return, with special observing techniques being put into operation. Meteors were counted in a very small restricted view so that the numbers were reduced to a reasonable level.

The radar method was in its infancy, but Hey, Parsons, and Stewart were able to measure the velocity of some Giacobinids by an unexpected and fortunate circumstance. No velocities had been measured in previous storms, so their measurements were a historic first. Nor has a swarm occurred since 1946, so their work is unique. Radar echoes were displayed as bright spots on a cathode-ray tube, with position indicating the range. The tube was photographed and the film moved at a slow but constant rate. Every echo that appeared during the progress of the shower was recorded as a dot on the film. Some of the meteors were extremely bright and generated a ball of ionization around the head of the meteor as it moved through the upper atmosphere. Usually a meteor reflects only when it is perpendicular to the antenna beam, but the head echo could be detected some time before the position of minimum range was reached and therefore showed as a curved track on the film as the range decreased with time. From the nature of the curve the velocity could be found with moderate accuracy. The velocity was 22.9 ± 1.3 km sec^{-1}, in agreement with the value predicted from the cometary orbit.

The single-station photographs from North Bay showed that the radiant was only 5 min from the expected position. This difference was smaller than the errors of measurement, so the meteoroids must have been moving in orbits that were exactly parallel to the orbit of the comet. The trails of most of the meteors appeared blurred on the photographs, with light showing in the spaces produced by the rotating shutter. Fragmentation was therefore occurring to a serious extent. The meteoroids were crumbling in the atmosphere, and the fragments were following behind the head to form a tail about 0.1 km in length. The freshly ejected material from the comet was a perfect example of the fragile dustball.

Despite the accurate methods of observation, no exact agreement was obtained on the rate. This may be due in part to the extremely short duration of the climax of the storm. Radar methods showed

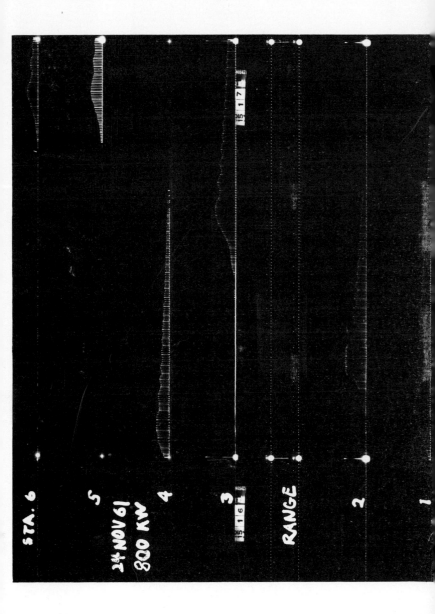

Figure 3.4. The Fresnel patterns obtained with a six-station radar. Courtesy Harvard College Observatory and the Smithsonian Astrophysical Observatory.

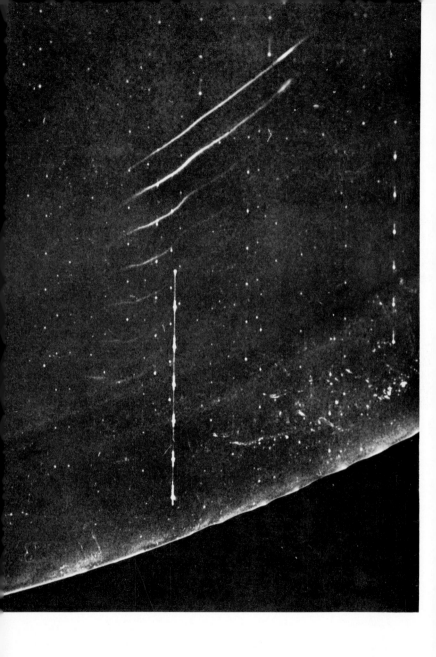

Figure 6.1. Successive images of a meteor train. *Courtesy Harvard College Observatory.*

Figure 8.1. Comet Mrkos 1957d. Courtesy *John A. Farrell.*

Figure 7.3. A thin section of a stone meteorite (Clovis, New Mexico) showing chondrules. *Courtesy Dr. E. P. Henderson, United States National Museum, Smithsonian Institution.*

that the rate was down by a factor of ⅓ at a time 5 minutes before and after the peak. If this is correct, more than 50 per cent of the meteoroids were encountered while the Earth moved a distance of 18,000 km in its orbit. Since the angle of approach of the swarm was inclined by 30 deg to the Earth's orbit, the thickness of the swarm was 9,000 km, which is less than the diameter of the Earth. When averaged over a 1-minute interval, radar gave an equivalent visual rate of 10,000 hr^{-1}, while averaged over a 10-minute interval the value was 7,000. Prentice in England gives the visual rate, after correcting for moonlight, as 2,250 hr^{-1}. Wylie reported a visual rate of 4,200 hr^{-1} in the United States. Over a 10-minute interval the equivalent visual rate reached 40,000 hr^{-1} as determined by the North Bay cameras, while Manning's 1-minute exposure in California gives 500,000 hr^{-1}. These differences may represent a genuine fine structure in the swarm with tightly packed clouds no more than 1,000 km thick. In retrospect it would have been advantageous if observers had taken a movie of the sky and counted the meteors frame by frame. The swarm was perturbed by Jupiter and missed the Earth at the 1959 return. Maybe a further perturbation will cause a storm again in the future, but this is unlikely.

A person interested in meteor showers does not have to wait for a storm to occur before taking up an active interest in the subject. Several meteor streams occur regularly each year, and the details are given in Table 4.2. These are "old faithfuls," and the results can almost be guaranteed if the correct date and the appropriate time of night are chosen. The word "transit" refers to the time when the radiant point of the meteor stream is crossing the celestial meridian. At this time the radiant is due south and reaches its highest elevation in the sky. The number of meteors varies approximately as sin θ, where θ is the elevation angle. The visual rate given in Table 4.2 is for the optimum condition at transit. Streams marked D are daytime streams and cannot be seen unless there happens to be a total eclipse of the sun. Streams marked S are in low southern declinations and are not visible from north temperate latitudes.

The reason for the regularity of the stream is connected with perturbations. Over a long period of time, gravitational and other disturbances separate the meteor particles and distribute them uniformly around the orbit. The ultimate fate of a meteor swarm is to be dispersed around the entire orbit, and this process is thought to take several hundred years to be accomplished. Each particle in the stream, of course, is moving with a velocity very close to the original velocity of the swarm, but the number of particles in a given volume of space is considerably reduced by the dispersal of the meteoroids.

TABLE 4.2   REGULAR STREAMS

STREAM	DATE AT MAXIMUM	DATE LIMITS	VISUAL RATE	TRANSIT, local time	RADIANT, R.A.Dec.	COMET
Quadrantids	Jan. 3	Jan. 1–Jan. 4	45	0828	230+48	?
Lyrids	Apr. 21	Apr. 19–Apr. 24	5	0359	270+33	1861 I
η Aquarids	May 4	Apr. 21–May 12	20	0736	336+00	Halley
Arietids D	June 8	May 29–June 18	60	0951	44+23	?
ζ Perseids D	June 9	June 1–June 16	40	1059	62+23	?
Ophiuchids S	June 20	June 17–June 26	20	2325	260—20	?
β Taurids D	June 30	June 24–July 6	20	1112	86+19	Encke
δ Aquarids	July 29	July 21–Aug. 15	15	0210	339—17	?
α Capricornids	Aug. 1	July 17–Aug. 21	5	0000	309—10	1948 n
ι Aquarids	Aug. 5	July 15–Aug. 25	5	0136	331—5	?
Perseids	Aug. 12	July 25–Aug. 17	50	0543	46+58	1862 III
κ Cygnids	Aug. 20	Aug. 18–Aug. 22	5	2125	289+56	?
Orionids	Oct. 22	Oct. 18–Oct. 26	20	0412	94+16	Halley
Taurids	Nov. 1	Sept. 15–Dec. 15	5	0042	51+14	Encke
Andromedids	Nov. 14	Nov. 3–Nov. 22	2	2220	22+27	Biela
Leonids	Nov. 17	Nov. 14–Nov. 20	5	0622	152+22	Temple
Phoenicids S	Dec. 5	Dec. 5–Dec. 5	50	2000	15—55	Blanpain
Geminids	Dec. 14	Dec. 7–Dec. 15	60	0201	113+32	?
Ursids	Dec. 22	Dec. 17–Dec. 24	5	0824	206+80	Tuttle

The perturbations also tend to produce slight distortions in the individual orbits, so that the radiant point becomes enlarged to become a finite but small area in the sky. Thus when the Earth passes through the orbit of a meteor stream each year, a modest reenactment of the storm is seen.

The Perseid stream is the best known. Meteors can be seen coming from the radiant north of Perseus for several weeks in July and August. At the maximum in the early morning hours of August 12 about 50 meteors hr^{-1} from the Perseid radiant can usually be seen, and perhaps some 15 or 20 more from the δ Aquarid stream and the sporadic complex. The Perseids move through the atmosphere with a velocity of 60 km sec^{-1} and therefore appear as rapid streaks in the sky. The speed is so great that the eye cannot follow the motion of the meteoroid and persistence of vision gives the impression of a streak.

The Perseid meteoroids are following in the orbit of the great Comet 1862 III. This comet has a period of 122 years, as determined from observations of the orbit. Its orbit is therefore almost parabolic, and there is considerable uncertainty in the period. The Perseid meteoroids make very infrequent visits to the sun; calculations show that the stream must be fairly old to be so uniformly spread around the comet orbit. It is conceivable that a Perseid swarm may exist at some position in the orbit, but if its period is measured in centuries, it may be some time before the Earth encounters it. There have been slight increases in Perseid activity; for example, in 1921 the rate was 250 hr^{-1}, and some researchers claim to find evidence for Perseid storms in the historic records that date back over a thousand years.

Two weeks before the Perseid maximum, the δ Aquarid stream can be seen. These meteors do not appear to full advantage in the Northern Hemisphere because of the low declination of the radiant. In the Southern Hemisphere the stream is comparable to the Perseids, but for northern observers the hourly rate is no more than 15. Nevertheless these meteors are quite distinctive, because they move more slowly and travel for longer distances across the sky. A δ Aquarid is usually slow enough to follow with the eyes, and is more typical of the popular description "shooting star."

The Orionids, like the Perseids, move with high velocity through the atmosphere. Visual observations have indicated a string of three or four separate radiant points for the Orionids, but photographic work has not confirmed this result. At one time it was thought that the Orionid meteors were connected with Halley's Comet, but again the photographic data has disproved this possibility.

While looking for Orionids, the observer may see a few Taurid meteors. This weak but long-duration stream reaches a broad maximum on November 1. Although the rate is seldom more than 5 hr^{-1}, the meteors can be distinguished because of their slow movement across the sky. A Taurid meteor appears as a moving blob among the stars, and some members of the stream show a distinct orange coloration. Another characteristic of the stream seems to be a higher percentage of bright meteors than normal. Although the rate is low, there is a good chance of seeing a meteor with negative magnitude from the stream. The Taurids follow a very complex pattern of paths scattered around the orbit of Comet Encke. The orbits are of low inclination to the plane of the solar system, and there is therefore a second intersection where the stream has crossed the orbit of the Earth, as shown in Figure 4.1. The second intersection occurs in late June, when the meteors are encountering the Earth after perihelion passage around the sun. The radiant point is therefore in the daytime sky and is observable only by radar techniques.

By the time the Geminids come along, the observer must be either of hardy stock or well protected from the weather in an observing enclosure. The stream is worth seeing, because the rate usually exceeds that of the Perseids and the radiant point passes almost overhead in north temperate latitudes. The velocity of the meteors is intermediate in value, 35 km sec^{-1}. The radiant is a well-defined area near Castor and Pollux in Gemini. This stream is not associated with any comet, a fact which might conceivably be used to argue against a cometary origin for meteors. Nor is the orbit of the Geminids similar to that of any known comet. The period of the meteoroids is 1.6 years, and the comet with one of the shortest periods is Encke, with 3.3 years. In support of the cometary origin it can only be concluded that at some time in the past a comet was thrown by perturbations into an orbit similar to that of the Geminids. In this extremely short-period orbit the comet would disintegrate rapidly, and the end product is represented by the Geminid stream. Plavec showed that the stream itself is suffering serious perturbations and that during the next century it may be expected to move out of range of the Earth's orbit.

The Ursid stream in late December has posed quite a problem. A minor stream at that date has been reported frequently since 1900, but in 1945 Czechoslovakian observers reported a rate of 169 hr^{-1}. Radar observations were difficult to make owing to the fact that the radiant point was in Ursa Minor and close to the Celestial Pole, but what observations were possible tended to disprove any high activity from the Ursids. Subsequent assessment of the data showed that the rate was probably no more than 40. Miss

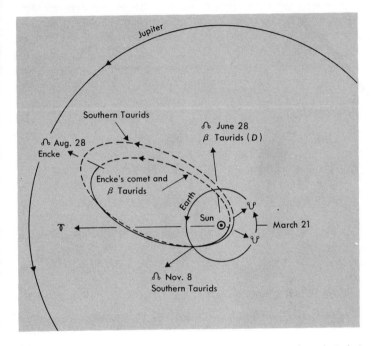

FIGURE 4.1   The orbit of the Taurid meteor stream. Orbit of Encke's Comet compared with that of the southern Taurid stream. The orbit of the daytime β Taurids corresponds closely with that of the comet; the ascending node for the β Taurids is indicated on the cometary orbit. *From Meteor Science and Engineering by D. W. R. McKinley. Copyright, 1961. McGraw-Hill Book Company. Used by permission.*

Mary Almond and I showed that the Ursids were moving in the orbit of Comet Tuttle. At the present time the stream shows very weak activity, and the 1945 data show at the most only a minor enhancement in the stream.

The Quadrantids are reserved for only the most tenacious of

visual observers. The stream occurs in the depth of winter, when frequent storms produce heavy cloud cover. The stream itself is of short duration, the maximum lasting for no more than 12 hours, so that there is only a 50 per cent chance that maximum activity will occur during the hours of darkness. The Quadrantids do, however, earn the classification of a major stream with a visual rate of 45, and at times several hundred meteors per hour have been reported. Like the Geminids, the Quadrantids do not follow the orbit of any comet observable at the present day. It must be concluded that the comet is defunct and has disintegrated, like Comet Biela and the parent comet of the Geminids.

※ **5** ※   **sporadic meteors**

The major meteor streams represent only a minority in the meteor population. Meteors that do not belong to the recognized streams are generally called *sporadic*, though perhaps the term "non-shower" would be more appropriate, because there is nothing occasional or intermittent in their nature. Although the Perseids, Geminids, and Quadrantids regularly each year produce meteors at a rate some 5 or 10 times greater than the rate of sporadic meteors, the total duration of a stream is short and the contribution to the meteor influx small. At least 80 per cent of the meteors observed in the night sky are not related to the major streams. Some of them form less active streams where the orbits are rather jumbled, and it is difficult to determine the average orbit of a stream member. If a considerable amount of work is carried out, there is no doubt that a large number of minor streams will be found among the sporadic meteors and patterns of movement will be disclosed. In this chapter, minor streams will be treated from the statistical point of view, that is to say, all meteors not belonging to the major streams will be classified as sporadic and discussed as a population. Any broad features found in sporadic meteors by this process automatically apply in general to the minor streams.

It has been very difficult to establish the simple influx law for sporadic meteors—the number of meteors with magnitude M that appear in 1 km^2 of the Earth's atmosphere during 1 hour. The trouble does not lie so much in the observations but in the analysis and interpretation. By 1958, members of the American Meteor Society had accumulated a total of 5,953 hours of observation spread fairly uniformly through the night and through the calendar year. During this period 71,431 meteors were observed, giving an average rate of 12 hr^{-1}. Canadian observers give a value that is somewhat lower than 12, and English observers find that the average rate is approximately 6. The differences are almost certainly brought about by the difference in observing conditions. In the higher latitudes the transparency of the atmosphere is not as great as in the central regions of the United States, and also interference is probably caused by the airglow and faint auroras. If the visual observations were continued for another 50 years, there would probably be little improvement on the A.M.S. value of 12 meteors hr^{-1} visible under good conditions.

But what is the collecting area of a visual observer? The retina of the human eye does not have the same sensitivity all over its surface. We see the faintest meteors only in the center of our field of view. If a fifth-magnitude meteor appears more than 10 deg away from the center of vision, it will probably not be seen. Meteors of zero magnitude are generally observed so long as they occur not more than 45 deg away from the center of vision, but at that point they appear, as the saying goes, in "the corner of the eye." As a further complication, it is not possible to clamp the eyes in a fixed direction; they tend to wander around, so that at times meteor observing degenerates into stargazing. As an approximation, it may be estimated that the eye covers a circle approximately 50 deg in diameter and detects all meteors in this circle with a magnitude of $+3.5$ or brighter. This cone corresponds to an area in the meteor layer of approximately 15,000 km^2 when the observer is looking at an elevation of 45 deg.

TABLE 5.1   INFLUX RATE OF SPORADIC METEORS *

Magnitude M	0	1	2	3	4	5
Hourly rate N	5.0×10^{-6}	2.9×10^{-5}	1.7×10^{-4}	6.5×10^{-4}	2.2×10^{-3}	7.2×10^{-3}

* The number per square kilometer per hour with visual magnitude brighter than or equal to M.

Determination of the visual influx is best done by a back-door approach. E. K. L. Upton and I took films from Super-Schmidt cameras covering a period of 93 hours. The area of the meteor layer covered by the camera was accurately known (5,980 km^2), and meteors were detected with uniform sensitivity all over this area. The photographic magnitude and other data could be accurately determined for the meteor. Thus the number of meteors per square kilometer per hour was found as a function of the photographic magnitude of the meteor. Previous calibrations had been made in which the visual observers' estimate of brightness was compared with the photographic determination, and the photographic magnitude could therefore be converted to the corresponding visual magnitude. As a result of this work, the influx rate of meteors as a function of visual magnitude is given in Table 5.1.

The table has some interesting features. The total area of the Earth's atmosphere at a height of 100 km is 5.26×10^8 km^2. It is easy to show that the number of meteors entering the Earth's atmosphere in 24 hours with a magnitude of $+5$ or brighter is approximately 90 million, truly a prodigious number when one realizes that these would all be visible if the Earth's surface could be covered with an efficient network of observers who were not troubled by cloud cover and daylight conditions. Assuming that the observers in the American Meteor Society worked to an effective limiting magnitude of $+3.5$, the average collecting area of an observer turns out to be 6,400 km^2, a reasonable value. The number of meteors in the table does not increase by the same factor from one magnitude to the next. Before converting to the visual scale, the ratio of increase was constant at 3.4 per magnitude. This apparent discrepancy in the visual numbers is due to an abnormality of the eye. The response of the retina is not exactly logarithmic, and Equation (1.1) does not hold exactly. At faint illuminations color vision ceases, and a meteor appears somewhat fainter than it should. For this reason it is preferable in exact work to use photographic or radio magnitudes.

The influx N (per square kilometer per hour) of meteors with a photographic magnitude equal to or brighter than P is given by the equation

$$\log_{10} N = 0.538P - 4.34 \tag{5.1}$$

This, of course, is an integrated total for meteors over the range of magnitude from P to $-\infty$. The equation for visual magnitude M is

$$\log_{10} N \simeq 0.538M - 5.17 \tag{5.2}$$

The rate given by Equations (5.1) and (5.2) is not exactly constant, having two main variations. Firstly the rate varies with the time of day (the diurnal variation), and secondly it varies from month to month through the year (the yearly variation). The diurnal variation is approximately sinusoidal, with a period of 24 hours, the maximum being at 6.00 A.M. The rate at 6.00 A.M. is approximately 2*N*, and the rate at 6.00 P.M. is approximately ½*N*. This variation is caused primarily by the motion of the Earth in its orbit around the sun. At 6.00 A.M. local time, the observer is facing the direction of the motion of the Earth, and under these conditions many more meteors are collected from space. Conversely, at 6.00 P.M. the observer is on the sheltered side of the Earth, and collisions of meteors with the Earth are less numerous.

The yearly variation is a slow change from month to month that is superimposed on the diurnal curve. It is caused by an actual difference in the numbers of sporadic orbits that are located in various positions around the sun. This segregation has been caused primarily by perturbation effects from the planets. Sporadic meteor activity reaches a broad maximum during the months of June, July, and August, when the rate may be as much as a factor of 2 greater than that predicted by Equation (5.1) and the included diurnal variation. The least prolific months are February, March, and April, when the sporadic meteor rates may be depressed by as much as a factor of 2. Of course, statistical variations are always to be expected, owing to the randomness of occurrence of the meteors in the sky. For example, if during the period of 1 hour the expected rate is 5, from the statistics of small numbers the total of meteors seen by various observers may be expected to differ by as much as ±50 per cent.

The number of meteors for an interval in magnitude dP may be found by differentiating Equation (5.1), when it will be found that

$$dN = ar^P dP \qquad (5.3)$$

This is an exponent law, and there is a factor of increase for each step of one magnitude. This factor is written as r and is equal to 3.4 or $\log^{-1}(0.538)$. The ratio r is a critical parameter for the meteor population. It can be shown that if $r > 2.5$, the total mass of meteoric material tends to infinity. The Super-Schmidt meteors used in determining the ratio had visual magnitudes between 0 and +4. Clearly, at some point fainter than magnitude +4 the ratio must decrease from 3.4 to 2.5 or less. However there is no evidence (even with radio data as faint as +12) of the ratio decreasing to the critical value.

Other methods of measurement confirm the ratio determined by Super-Schmidt cameras. Early visual data tended to indicate a value $r \doteqdot 2.5$, though a careful consideration by E. J. Opik of all the factors affecting visual determinations has increased this estimate to 3.3. In the same way, telescopic observations between magnitude +5 and +8 at first gave the comfortable mathematical value 2.5, but later analysis shows that r is between 3 and 4.

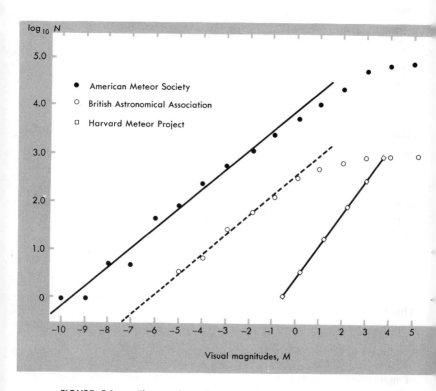

FIGURE 5.1   The number of meteors N seen with magnitude brighter than M.

There is a decrease in the ratio for meteors brighter than magnitude 0. The magnitude distribution of 71,431 meteors observed by the American Meteor Society is given in Figure 5.1. The gradient of the line from magnitude −10 to −2 corresponds to

$r = 2.5$. This is confirmed by a smaller number of visual observations obtained by members of the British Astronomical Association. These results are also shown in Figure 5.1. Although the British data are less numerous, they are more accurate. The results were obtained with a network where the meteor was observed by two or more observers at spaced stations. The Super-Schmidt data on the other hand show a decidedly steeper curve for the fainter meteors. One concludes that there is a decided difference in the magnitude distributions between ordinary visual meteors and the brighter fireballs. Somewhere between magnitude −5 and 0 the value of r has changed from 2.5 to 3.4. I have placed the cross-over point somewhat arbitrarily at −3, and I attribute the difference to the origin of the meteoroids.

The magnitude law for fireballs is exactly what would be expected if the mass distribution of the particles followed the same law as that of meteorites. For meteorites, the number with mass $\geqslant m$ is proportional to $1/m$, and from Equation (2.11) it can be shown that $r = 2.5$. The same mass law is also exhibited by the asteroidal fragments moving in the space between the planets. This has confirmed the belief that meteorites are nothing more than asteroidal fragments. The similarity in the law for fireballs suggests that fireballs are also related to asteroids and meteorites. Thus, meteors with magnitudes brighter than the planet Venus are most probably caused by a solid chunk of rock or iron entering the atmosphere. In fact, calculations show that a meteor of magnitude −10 probably deposited on the Earth's surface a specimen of mass 20 or 30 lb.

The steepness of the curve for fainter meteors indicates a different origin. It also shows graphically how the fainter visual meteors are dominated by asteroidal fragments for magnitudes brighter than −3 and yet themselves dominate the meteor population at faint magnitudes. The mass law for faint meteors is similar to the one expected from comets; in fact, F. L. Whipple has shown that there is a certain upper limit to the mass that may be ejected from a cometary nucleus. It is not surprising, therefore, to find large numbers of cometary meteors in any photographic sample.

When the masses of individual meteors are determined, the flux per square kilometer per year can be given as a function of mass:

$$\log_{10} N = 0.4 - 1.34 \log_{10} m \qquad (5.4)$$

The number N is cumulative; it is the total number with mass $\geqslant m$ g.

Before World War II the vast majority of sporadic meteors were thought to be interstellar in origin. Meteoroids were thought to be in open orbits crossing the Earth's orbit, with speeds in excess of the parabolic limit as given in Equation (1.2). This was a surprising turn for meteor astronomy from two points of view; in the first place the result was totally false, and it is of interest to see how such a wrong conclusion could be drawn, while in the second place the conclusion attracted great attention because it held out the possibility for astrophysicists to deal directly with material from the realm of the stars.

The conclusion was arrived at entirely on the basis of visual observations, and the error was caused primarily by the inaccuracies of this method. Direct measurements had been made on many meteors and fireballs in their passage through the atmosphere. G. von Niessl collected together all available observations on bright fireballs up until 1925, and from eye-witness accounts of the angular motion and time of flight computed the velocity of each object. He found 79 per cent of the fireballs to be interstellar in origin with hyperbolic velocities. Unfortunately it is now known that an eye witness tends to exaggerate the length of flight and to underestimate the duration of the phenomena. These two effects together automatically ensure an overestimate of velocity. Even today visual estimates are unreliable in this respect, and von Niessl's catalog of objects is worthless from the quantitative point of view. Direct measurements using a rocking mirror also gave a high percentage of interstellar meteors, but here again there were peculiar subjective errors entailed in the use of this device. Unfortunately the systematic errors caused a gross overestimate in the speed of the meteor. As with the fireball catalog, early results from the rocking-mirror technique have to be discounted.

Many observers gave strong support for the existence of interstellar meteors by a simple yet indirect method. Suppose that meteoroids are approaching the Earth uniformly from all directions. The Earth is moving around its orbit at a velocity of approximately

30 km sec^{-1}, and there will be a tendency for it to sweep up more meteoroids on the hemisphere which faces in the direction of the motion. A straightforward calculation shows that the rate of meteors detected at 6.00 A.M. will be at least 10 times greater than the rate at 6.00 P.M., if the velocity of the meteors is less than the parabolic limit. If an observer simply counts meteors throughout the night, the increase in rate between evening and dawn will define for him the mean velocity of meteoroids. Thus, after many years of counting, visual observers had established beyond doubt that the rate increased by a factor of no more than 5 between the evening and the morning hours. With unswerving logic it was concluded that the speed of meteors must be considerably greater than the parabolic limit, otherwise such great numbers would not be seen in the evening hours. Unfortunately there was a serious fallacy in the argument that was later to be uncovered. Meteoroids do not approach the Earth uniformly from all directions; in fact there is a great preponderance of them moving so as to overtake the Earth. This vitiates the initial premise and hence the conclusions drawn from the observations.

After World War II radio meteor techniques were in their infancy, and it was not possible to measure the orbits of individual sporadic meteors. The interstellar problem was therefore tackled by two relatively indirect methods, the velocity-distribution and the radiant-distribution methods. The simplest test to apply to the velocity distribution was to look for meteors with velocities greater than 72 km sec^{-1}. The velocity of a meteor in a parabolic orbit is 42 km sec^{-1}, measured with respect to the sun. The velocity of the Earth is on the average 29.8 km sec^{-1}, and the maximum speed of a meteor in the atmosphere will be produced by a head-on collision. Under these conditions the velocity will be 72 km sec^{-1}. More than 11,000 meteor velocities were measured at Ottawa between 1948 and 1950, and although many stream meteors were included in the sample, the number did contain a large proportion of sporadic meteors. There was no doubt that if interstellar meteors occurred in any great numbers, they would be evident in the velocity distribution. However, less than 1 per cent of the meteors showed velocities greater than 72 km sec^{-1}. The error of measurement for a single velocity was ±4 km sec^{-1}, and a small percentage above the parabolic limit could adequately be accounted for in terms of observational error. Similar observations were made at Manchester, England, where a special program was maintained to compare the dusk and dawn hours. Again the number of interstellar meteors detected was no more than would be expected by chance from the known observational errors.

Concurrently with the velocity measurements, I made a survey of the radiant distribution of sporadic meteors. If sporadic meteors were truly interstellar in origin, it would be reasonable to expect some evidence for interstellar streaming and some preferential directions for the arrival of meteors from between the stars. As a secondary result, the survey would provide a check for the original assumption in the visual data that meteors were approaching the Earth uniformly from all directions. Two fixed antennas were set to point as close to the horizon as possible, and echoes were recorded in each. The antennas effectively provided two windows in the sky, and sporadic radiants could be counted as they were carried across the window by the rotating of the celestial sphere. A large grouping of radiants would produce echoes first on one antenna and then on the other, so that the time delay gave a measure of the declination of the group. After a survey which lasted for 24 months, I found a definite pattern among the sporadic radiants. There was a concentration of radiant points in the plane of the ecliptic, and three "hot spots" were located along the ecliptic.

Throughout the year the Earth was bombarded by meteors from three distinct directions which were fixed with respect to the sun. Each night a concentration of radiant points showed up, and the hot spot in the sky was due south of the observer at 2.00 A.M. local time. A corresponding concentration occurred during the daytime, passing the due south point at 10.00 A.M.; the third concentration was in transit at 6.00 A.M. The last concentration was the one expected from earlier theoretical considerations, and it corresponded to meteor particles that were being swept up by the motion of the Earth. The concentration was centered at the apex of the Earth's motion in its orbit around the sun. The other two concentrations were unexpected, and their existence was the death knell for the hypothesis of interstellar meteors. Since these radiant concentrations maintained a fixed position relative to the sun (as the Earth moved in a complete circle around its orbit), they could not be caused by interstellar meteors. The antihelion concentration, approximately opposite to the sun and in transit a little after midnight, was caused by meteoroids moving toward the sun in elliptical orbits. The daytime concentration, some 30 deg from the sun, was caused by meteors crossing the orbit of the Earth after passing perihelion. A further analysis showed that the day and night concentrations were caused by a rosette of elliptical orbits set in all directions around the sun, and the average shape of the orbit was something like that of the Geminid meteor stream. Since the radiant concentrations near the sun and antihelion point were in the plane of the ecliptic, it was clear that the meteoroids were in low-inclination orbits and were associated with the solar system. Thus both the velocity distributions and the radiant distributions gave independent confirmation for a solar-system origin of sporadic meteors.

The numbers of meteors moving in direct orbits, in the same direction of revolution as the Earth, was surprisingly large. It is very difficult to obtain an exact estimate of the ratio between direct and retrograde orbits, because extremely large correction factors are involved. However, the best estimates that can be made show that for meteors with mass greater than 10 mg the percentage of directly moving orbits in space is greater than 99. From this result it is presumed that the majority of sporadic meteors are injected into the solar system in directly moving orbits from the short-period comets. These comets are predominantly direct in their motion. If any meteor is injected or perturbed so as to move against the main stream of particles, the probability of collision is large, and the meteoroid is quickly destroyed. Furthermore the sweeping action of the planets is more serious for a retrograde particle; directly moving particles tend to move along with the planets and avoid capture.

Super-Schmidt cameras and the multistation radar system have provided thousands of orbits measured for individual meteors. Thus the problem of sporadic meteors has now become much more exact, since the average properties of groups of meteors no longer have to be measured. The photographic data reach to a limiting magnitude of $+4$ while the radio data extend at the present time to $+12$.

Although the general results obtained by the two methods are similar, there are notable differences, and it is convenient to separate the photographic from the radio data. The most frequent value for semimajor axis among photographic meteors is 3.0, corresponding to a period of a little over 5 years. Without further evidence it would be difficult to decide between an asteroidal or cometary origin for sporadic meteors. The period is close to that of the short-period comets, yet the aphelion point is at the asteroid zone. However, the fragile, crumbly nature of the meteoroids, the demonstrated relationship between stream and meteors and comets, and the similarity between stream and sporadic orbits all point in favor of a cometary origin. The most frequent value of eccentricity among sporadic orbits is 0.9, which is more in agreement with the value for short-period comets. The orbits of sporadic meteors are spread some 30 deg in inclination on either side of the ecliptic, whereas the orbits of asteroids are confined within narrower limits of inclination.

Radio meteors show slightly different orbital properties. The difference in shape of the orbit is interpreted as being a real result and not due to observational selection caused by the radio technique. Meteors with a visual magnitude of approximately $+10$ show orbits that are shorter in period and less elliptical than those of the photographic meteors. The most frequent value of semimajor axis found is $a = 2$, corresponding to a period of 3 years. The eccentricities are generally smaller, and the orbit therefore tends to be more circular than the orbit of the photographic meteor. The aphelion of these meteors is close to the orbit of Mars rather than to the asteroid zone. Radio meteors are thought to have been considerably disturbed in their orbits by physical effects in the solar system. One serious disturbance is the decrease in angular momentum caused by radiation from the sun. If light or corpuscles from the sun are absorbed by a meteoroid and reradiated isotropically, then there is a net decrease in the momentum of the meteoroid. The effect was first discussed by Poynting and Robertson, who derived the result from the equations of special relativity. Although the meteoroid is radiating isotropically as seen from a moving coordinate system, there is a slight concentration of the scattered light in the direction of motion of the meteoroid when viewed from a fixed frame of reference. This slight enhancement in the scattered intensity is the cause of the reduction in momentum of the meteoroid. Ultimately, a particle in a long elliptical orbit is made to spiral in toward the sun. The long elliptical orbit becomes progressively shorter and more circular. Although the Poynting-Robertson effect works in the right direction for explaining the difference between the photographic and radio orbits, it is not certain at the present time whether this is indeed the cause of the differences in the two populations.

Among faint meteors an additional and perplexing component has been found in the population. At approximately magnitude $+7$, corresponding to a mass of a few milligrams, the toroidal group begins to appear. These meteors become more important at the fainter magnitudes, until at magnitude $+10$ the toroidal group may comprise some 30 per cent of all sporadic meteors. A typical meteor in this group has an orbit with $a = 1$ and $e = 0.3$, and an inclination of 60 deg. The orbits are almost circular and highly inclined to the plane of the solar system. If visualized as being set in all positions around the orbit of the Earth, the family of orbits would appear rather like the basket-weave coils familiar in the early days of wireless telegraphy. These coils were sometimes called "toroidal," and the group of meteors has been named accordingly.

The toroidal group is very perplexing to students of meteor astronomy and celestial mechanics. It is easy to imagine meteor particles injected by short-period comets and therefore following orbits in the plane of the solar system. However it is difficult to imagine a mechanism for disturbing comets so that they move almost at right angles to the plane of the solar system. Very few short-period comets are known in orbits with high inclination, but of course it is possible that a large comet existed with such an orbit in the past and that the toroidal group represents the remnants of this lost comet. On the other hand some astronomers are working with the idea that the meteors were originally located in the plane of the solar system and have been subsequently tilted by perturbations from Jupiter and other planets.

※ 6 ※

meteors
and
the
atmosphere

In Chapter 2 the interaction of a meteor with the atmosphere was described. A meteoroid spans thousands, perhaps even millions, of years in the quietness of interplanetary space, then is spectacularly destroyed in a fraction of a second. Somewhat ironically, we learn more physics during the brief flash of a meteor than we do from its entire previous history. We learn facts concerning the physics of the upper atmosphere and also gain knowledge of the meteoroid itself; in fact the properties of the atmosphere and of the meteoroid are very difficult to separate from each other. The average heights of meteor trails are given in Table 6.1.

TABLE 6.1   **AVERAGE HEIGHT OF METEOR TRAILS ***

VELOCITY, km sec^{-1}	BEGINNING HEIGHT, km	HEIGHT AT MAXIMUM LIGHT, km	END HEIGHT, km
10	80	75	70
20	91	86	80
30	96	91	86
40	101	95	90
50	104	99	94
60	108	102	97
70	110	105	100

* Visual magnitude $+3$.

In the 1930s Fred L. Whipple began the first serious attempt to study the upper atmosphere from meteor observations. Admittedly this idea had been used before, by Brandes and Benzenberg as far back as the late eighteenth century, for example. It was realized that at whatever height the meteor was seen, there must be appreciable atmosphere present. This fact established beyond doubt the qualitative fact that the atmosphere extended at least to a height of 60 miles, much further than was suspected hitherto. Whipple however used the meteor as a natural probe and attempted to measure atmospheric densities quantitatively.

Before the satellite era, meteors were the best available method for determining densities. The velocity of sound waves carried through the high atmosphere and the scattering of sunlight were other, but less reliable, methods. The idea behind the "meteor probe" was simple enough. The mass of the object could be found from the total light emitted during its passage through the atmosphere. This was equivalent to integrating Equation (2.4). The atmospheric density could then be determined from the measured rate of deceleration by using the drag equation [Equation (2.2)]. Air densities were indeed determined in this manner within the meteor layer between 70 and 120 km above the surface of the Earth. Subsequent work with satellites has shown that the early density determinations were accurate to within an order of magnitude.

The method was fraught with difficulties, however, and has gladly been abandoned now that satellites are moving through the fringe of the atmosphere. Some of the pitfalls illustrate the dangers in a model that is too simple and also indicate the unexpected tricks that Nature can play on a scientist. The classical theory applies exactly to a uniform symmetrical object, such as a ball bearing. Slight variations in shape can also be taken into account in the theory, but the theory does not make allowances for fragmentation. The ablation coefficient that would naturally be chosen is the energy required to vaporize the meteor material. When fragments become dislodged, the ablation coefficient ζ is reduced, and it is impossible to assign a reliable value. So far as the density of the meteoroid was concerned, it was natural to presume that ρ would lie somewhere between the density of stone, 2.5 g cm^{-3}, and the density of solid iron, 9 g cm^{-3}. It was rather capricious of Nature to provide material that had a density of 0.4 g cm^{-3}, or possibly less! The air density depended critically on the calculated mass of the meteoroid, which in turn depended on the luminous efficiency τ. Theoretical estimates of the value of τ were available in the 1930s, but this has proved to be an extremely difficult quantity to calculate from physical theory. The only reliable way to determine it was to fire into the atmosphere an artificial meteoroid of known mass. Of course, this was not done until the satellite era, in 1962. All these problems added together made the meteoroid a very unsatisfactory probe for determining atmospheric densities.

The glowing train produced by a bright meteor has been very

useful for determining winds in the upper atmosphere. The meteor acts as a line probe extending into the atmosphere for 10 or 20 km. The glowing train is at first perfectly straight, but as time passes it becomes twisted by the upper-atmosphere winds. The motion of the train can be followed by cameras on the ground, and a movement of only a few meteors can easily be measured. Unfortunately meteor trains are a rare phenomenon, and the collection of wind data has been extremely slow.

An example of train photography is shown in Figure 6.1. Seven images of the train can be made out on the original film; they appear side by side in the photograph because the camera was displaced every few seconds. Analyses of photographs like this have revealed very strong winds. Speeds of 50 m sec^{-1}, or 300 mph, are the rule rather than the exception. The wind blows horizontally most of the time—there are very few updrafts or downdrafts. There are drastic changes in direction and speed over a fairly small change in height.

A typical plot of wind velocity as a function of height is shown in Figure 6.2. Between a height of 86 and 109 km the wind has reversed its direction 5 times. At any given height the wind speed and direction persists for several minutes, and so a shear is established in the upper atmosphere. The wind at a height of 100 km in Figure 6.2 is blowing in the opposite direction from the wind at a height of 94 km, and the two wind streams are slipping past each other. This condition sets up turbulence within the various wind layers, and the stirring motion tends to break up the meteor train. The turbulence also mixes and spreads the ionization within the ionosphere.

The motion of meteor trails can also be observed by radio methods. In England and the United States systematic measurements have been made on upper-atmosphere winds by this method. The winds have been found to show a surprising regularity in their behavior from day to day. Although their direction changes markedly during the course of the day, the same pattern is likely to occur on the following day. In fact, detailed analyses have been made to uncover the diurnal variations in the wind pattern.

The radio echo from an average meteor decreases rapidly, usually lasting for no more than 0.5 seconds. A time-dependent decay term should be added to Equation (3.4) to account for the decrease in echo amplitude after the Fresnel pattern has been formed. This decrease is approximately exponential with time and is due to the expansion of a column of ionization. So long as the column is less than $\lambda/2\pi$ in diameter, the individual electrons reflect in phase with each

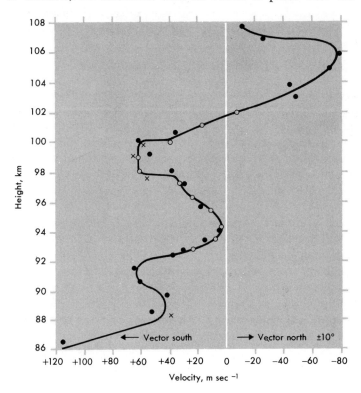

FIGURE 6.2   Profiles of wind velocity in the upper atmosphere. Variation of train velocity with height, from a Super-Schmidt meteor-train sequence taken in Massachusetts, August 13, 1950. *Courtesy F. L. Whipple.*

other. As the diameter of the column increases, a phase difference is established between the electrons nearest to the radar and the electrons on the opposite side of the column. Thus the rate of decay of the echo gives a measure of the rate of expansion of the column of ionization. This in turn is a function of the rate of diffusion of ions in the upper atmosphere. From the decay of meteor echoes, the diffusion coefficient at various heights within the meteor layer and for various seasons of the year can be determined. Once again the meteor has provided a useful probe.

The measurements of diffusion have given confirmation to the measurements of atmospheric density and temperature made by other methods. The results of all available investigations are summarized in the adopted "Standard Atmosphere," published by the United States Air Force. The diffusion rate of meteor trails is consistent with the temperatures, mean chemical constituents, and pressures of the standard atmosphere. They also consisted with the assumption that the meteor trails are not very much hotter than the surrounding atmosphere. This is a somewhat surprising result, since we have seen in Chapter 2 that most of the kinetic energy of the meteoroid is dissipated as heat. Presumably the excess temperature associated with the meteor is rapidly reduced by radiation and conduction.

The ionosphere surrounding the Earth is of great benefit to mankind. The ionized layer, consisting of positive ions and electrons, behaves like a mirror in the sky. The electrons in the ionosphere vibrate in synchronism with a radio signal sent from the Earth. The vibrating electron is then able to reradiate the signal back to a different part of the Earth. Without the ionosphere, short-wave communication around the Earth would be impossible. It is well established that the ionosphere, is produced and maintained by radiation from the sun. The ultraviolet wavelengths in particular supply sufficient energy to ionize oxygen and nitrogen atoms in the upper atmosphere, thus producing the ionosphere. But what happens when the sun goes down? Surprisingly enough, the ionosphere persists throughout the hours of darkness. The electron density decreases by approximately an order of magnitude, but calculations show that recombination should cause a much greater decrease in the ionization. Thus without an additional supply of energy one would naturally expect the ionosphere to disappear at night and radio communications to cease.

Many authors have tried to prove that the additional source of energy is provided by meteors, and an almost equal number have tried to disprove this idea. At the present time the argument is inconclusive because of insufficient facts concerning the meteors themselves. Certainly the measurements of the total flux of meteors give a value of 10^7 or 10^8 g day^{-1} falling on the Earth as a whole. Under various assumptions of ionizing probability and recombination coefficient, this flux is capable of producing between 10^3 and 10^7 electrons m^{-3} sec^{-1}. At a value of 10^3 electrons m^{-3} sec^{-1}, the meteors will make only a small contribution to the ionosphere, and some other source for nighttime ionization must be found. If the figure 10^7 electrons m^{-3} sec^{-1} is correct, the nighttime ionization can be easily maintained by the meteoric influx. Further work will probably show that meteors are indeed quite important in maintaining the nighttime ionosphere.

Do meteors affect the troposphere, the lower atmosphere? For many years controversy has raged over this question. On the one hand some scientists argue that meteor dust and fragments slowly fall from the meteor layer and pass through the lower atmosphere on the way to the ground. Most of our weather, good and bad, is produced in the troposphere, the region below the height of about 10 miles. When storms develop, masses of warm moist air become cooled, and the moisture condenses into water droplets. At first the water droplets form tenuous clouds, then as the process continues, heavy mist and raindrops form. It is well known from the physics of vapors that condensation does not take place readily in a pure vapor. A foreign object or "nucleus" is needed to speed up the condensation process. The vapor condenses more readily on a surface of the nucleus, and gradually the nucleus is enveloped by a drop of liquid. Although every raindrop probably contains a condensation nucleus, it is very difficult to find it because of its microscopic size. It is generally supposed that condensation nuclei are provided by ordinary dust blown from the desert regions, industrial particles, and solidified salt spray from the oceans.

It is only a short step to postulate that meteor dust can provide condensation nuclei for clouds. To investigate the postulate, rainfall records should, ideally, be very closely examined to try to determine a correlation between the regular meteor streams, such as the Perseids, and the onset of heavy rainfall over the surface of the Earth. Ideally an attempt would be made to look inside a raindrop and locate the original meteoritic nucleus, but so much pollution and so many other contaminants are present that the task is hopeless. Again, condensation might be experimentally induced in a small chamber at the surface of the Earth, and the number of nuclei present from day to day might be counted.

All these methods of proving the connection between meteors and rainfall have been used by proponents of the theory, and some of the methods, particularly the statistical correlation of meteor streams with rainfall, have been used by its opponents. As with the ionosphere, at the present time the scientific debate is still in progress, and no sure conclusion has been reached.

E. G. Bowen has analyzed rainfall records for the past 100 years for places scattered over the entire globe. He has established to his own satisfaction that heavy rainfall has occurred in both the Southern and Northern Hemispheres approximately 30 days after the occurrence of a meteor stream. His correlation between the rainfall in the Southern Hemisphere and the Geminid and Ursid meteor streams has been given much attention. Also his correlation of heavy precipitation in January in northern Europe following the Geminid stream in December is fairly well established.

F. L. Whipple and I have criticized the correlation from the astronomical point of view. The Geminids and Ursids are meteor streams of the Northern Hemisphere, and the radiant point is low on the horizon in the areas in which Bowen was obtaining a correlation. Thus, though few Geminids or Ursids occur over the Southern Hemisphere, Bowen has concluded that they cause heavy rainfall in these regions. There is no evidence for pronounced mixing of the upper atmosphere between the Northern and Southern hemispheres, and therefore it seems very unlikely that a northern meteor stream could produce such rainfall. The correlation of rainfall in northern Europe with the Geminids has been criticized by meteorologists. A detailed study of weather maps on successive years for the month of January shows that a fairly characteristic weather pattern develops during the second week of the month. It is true that the frontal systems dumped precipitation on northern Europe on the dates predicted by the meteor-dust theory; this precipitation, however, is certainly a result of the winter pattern itself and not of "cloud seeding," because the precipitation at that period is not much worse than that of an average storm. The cause of the tendency of the weather pattern to repeat from year to year is not well known, and there are, of course, similar weather patterns which tend to repeat at other dates during the year and also have no explanation at the present time. It is hardly likely that the weather pattern itself could be a product of meteoritic dust.

It has been argued that meteor streams do not substantially increase the rate of influx of meteoritic debris. A glance at Table 1.2 will show that the hourly rate of meteors as seen by a visual observer does not increase by more than a factor of 3 or 4 during major streams such as the Perseids or Geminids, so it is very difficult to explain how a relatively small increase in the general meteor activity could trigger heavy rainfall. Proponents of the rainfall hypothesis have suggested that perhaps the meteor streams carry with them a large number of very small particles that are not seen by a visual observer, but this argument has been adequately refuted by radio observations. Radar equipment is able to observe meteors far below the visual threshold down to magnitudes of $+10$ and $+15$, and the major streams are shown to be deficient in small meteoroids. Proponents of the rainfall theory have suggested that meteor debris from the streams is much more efficient at forming a condensation at nucleus than meteor debris from sporadic meteors. In effect they propose a chemical differentiation between sporadic and stream meteors. Although this would indeed be a feasible explanation of the results, there seems to be no way of reconciling this suggestion with the astronomical data. Meteor streams are ejected from comets, and sporadic meteors are formed by perturbations of the streams, thus they should be chemically identical.

Perhaps the most damning evidence against the postulated connection between meteor streams and rainfall is the phenomenon of a meteor storm. The great meteor swarms mentioned in Chapter 4 have collided with the Earth on several occasions during the past century. When this occurs, the Earth is bombarded with much more material than it receives from an annual stream such as the Perseids or Geminids. The rate of arrival of material may increase a thousandfold or even more in a matter of a few hours. These events therefore provide a crucial test for the theory, for torrential rainfall would be expected to result from such a sudden increase in meteor dust. Yet the rainfall records have been singularly uninteresting during the 30 days following each of the major swarms.

The Andromedid storm of 1872, for example, was followed 30 days later by a decrease rather than an increase in the average precipitation. The Giacobinids of this century, in 1933 and 1946, produced no abnormalities in the rainfall record. There was so much debris from the Giacobinids in 1946 that for several hours a general increase in the electron content in the ionosphere was maintained, which never happens during the annually occurring major streams, and yet the lower atmosphere and troposphere showed no effects.

It is conceivable that a meteor could cause a minor fluctuation in the Earth's magnetic field. For example, if the meteoroid built up an electric charge in space, it would behave as a moving charge as it passed through the upper atmosphere. Again, it might be possible for electrostatic potential to develop between various layers in the upper atmosphere and for a discharge to take place when the ion column of the meteor provided a conducting path between the layers. Speculations such as these, along with other more fanciful theories, have been considered as a mechanism for producing a magnetic field from a meteor. But before a theorist goes too far in developing a theory, it is prudent to make some observations to see whether any effect indeed exists.

Kalashnikov in Russia devised a simple experiment in which a large coil 300 m in diameter was attached to a sensitive galvanometer. According to Kalashnikov, the galvanometer was observed to kick when a meteor appeared in the sky, thus indicating that the meteor had produced a pulse in the magnetic field of the Earth. In New Mexico I repeated Kalashnikov's experiment, using a low-noise amplifier and automatic pen recorder instead of a galvanometer. I found that one meteor in three did indeed coincide with a pulse in the magnetic field. A careful analysis, however, showed that this correlation was just the amount to be expected from the random occurrence of meteors and a random occurrence of magnetic noise pulses. Thus I concluded that a visual meteor (with magnitude brighter than $+5$) did not produce a pulse greater than the noise level of the equipment, which was 2×10^{-8} gauss.

A different experiment was carried out later in the United States by Jenkins, Phillips, and Maple. The fluctuating electric signal from the large coil was amplified and recorded. This signal was then fed to a spectrum analyzer which was sensitive to certain selected frequencies. They found a definite correlation in the general magnetic noise level during periods of major meteor showers such as the

Geminids. The correlation was most pronounced in the channel tuned to a frequency of 1.5 cps. This did not show, of course, that an individual meteor caused a noise pulse. The enhancement of the noise level was less than the minimum signal detectable by earlier workers.

Using a sensitive magnetometer and a radar system for observing meteors, Ellyett and Fraser in New Zealand have made a more detailed investigation. The magnetometer had a narrow bandwidth of 0.3 cps, which decreased the limiting sensitivity to 5×10^{-10} gauss. This is nearly two orders of magnitude more sensitive than the early systems, though this increase in sensitivity will be realized only if the meteor itself produces a narrow band signal. The frequency of the magnetometer was set at 1.5 cps to be in the region of interest discovered by Jenkins, Phillips, and Maple.

No increase in the magnetic noise level was noticed during times of increased meteor rates. It must be pointed out, though, that no observations were carried out during the major streams such as the Perseids and Geminids, and so this result does not necessarily disagree with the results in the United States. Nothing unusual was found in the magnetic record coincident with the appearance of most of the meteors. One meteor in 10, on the average, did correlate with a pulse in the magnetic record, and a careful statistical analysis showed that this rate of correlation was a little greater than could be expected from the laws of chance. Furthermore the number of correlations between meteor echoes and magnetic disturbances were greater for the brighter meteors. This adds support to the conclusion that some meteors may produce small disturbances in the magnetic field of the Earth. The meteors observed in the New Zealand experiment were between magnitude $+8$ and $+10$. Even so, theorists would be well advised to withhold their efforts in this area until the observational data become a little more exciting.

Many eye-witness accounts refer to sounds that were heard when a bright fireball traveled across the sky. It is very startling to see such an apparition, and no doubt many people have imagined a rushing or a sizzling sound to accompany what they saw. However there seem to be too many otherwise reliable reports to be explained away in this manner. If the sound does accompany the fireball, we have a rather difficult problem in physics, for with the known speed of sound the fireball should be heard at least 5 minutes *after* it has appeared and not while it is moving across the sky.

An immediate suggestion which comes to mind is that radio signals are produced and that these are somehow converted into sound in the vicinity of the observer. Such a phenomenon is known to take place in the vicinity of high-power radio transmitters. Even a bad filling in a tooth can on very rare occasions act as a detector and provide audible sounds for the fortunate (or unfortunate) owner.

Measurements have been made between the frequencies of 500 and 30 mcs with meteors of magnitude fainter than -3. The results at the higher frequencies were negative, and the conclusion was that less than 10^{-18} of the original kinetic energy of the meteor is converted into electromagnetic radiation in a bandwidth of 1 cps. At 30 mcs a small amount of radio noise has been observed simultaneously with the occurrence of a meteor. These events are rare, and it has not been possible to rule out the chance of a stray reflection of a man-made signal from the ion column of the meteor. Thus the emission from an average meteor is at best very weak. This does not preclude the possibility that a very bright fireball, say, of magnitude -25, could produce a strong radio field. Bright fireballs are extremely rare and because of this fact have not yet been observed by a waiting radio system. Theoretical physicists would be pleased to develop a detailed explanation of the phenomena if quantitative measurements were ever made. The ionization surrounding the meteoroid provides a very dense plasma, and rapid oscillations in this plasma would certainly be expected.

Neumann bands

Crystal cleavage plane

Crystal cleavage plane

Figure 7.4. The Mayodan hexahedrite meteorite showing Neumann bands.
Courtesy Dr. E. P. Henderson, United States National Museum, Smithsonian
Institution.

Figure 7.5. A meteorite showing Widmänstatten figures. *Courtesy American Museum of Natural History, New York.*

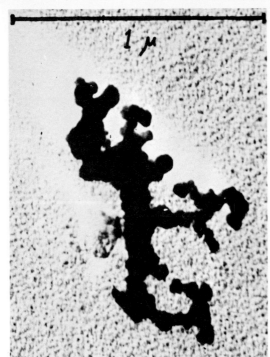

Figure 7.6. A fluffy micro-meteorite. (Right). Courtesy Dr. C. L. Hemenway, Dudley Observatory.

Figure 7.7. A compact micrometeorite. (Below). Courtesy Dr. C. L. Hemenway, Dudley Observatory

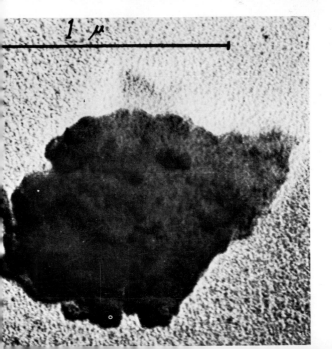

Figure 7.8. A micrometeorite spherule. *Courtesy Dr. C. L. Hemenway, Dudley Observatory.*

meteorites
and
micrometeorites

Once a year, on the average, a meteorite falls on the continent of North America and is recovered. Most United States meteorites have been recovered from the central plains, because it is easier to locate an object when it has fallen on a plowed field or pasture than when it has fallen in a mountainous and forested region. The black spots in Figure 7.1 show the places where meteorites have fallen in the Great Plains since the time of colonization of the continent. A glance at the map shows a concentration of meteorites toward the eastern seaboard, but this does not mean that the fall of meteorites is selective. One must remember that during the past

FIGURE 7.1   Meteorite falls in the United States.

200 years the population in the United States has spread westward and that there has always been a greater number of people per square mile on the eastern side, which makes the chance of recovering a meteorite there correspondingly greater.

We have seen in Chapter 5 how a meteorite is different in origin from a meteor. A fireball brighter than magnitude −3 is more likely to be a solid chunk of stone and iron than the fluffy object that belongs to the meteor streams. If a fireball is very bright, with a magnitude of −10 or greater, it is almost certainly produced by a meteorite, and the object will have fallen to Earth somewhere after the fireball has ceased to shine.

To find a meteorite in the United States is perhaps more difficult than finding a needle in a haystack. If many people have observed a bright fireball, it is possible to calculate the trajectory of the object and predict approximately the area in which it has fallen. Even so it is very difficult to locate the object. Most meteorites have been recovered because they fell fairly close to a person. The average distance between a meteorite that has fallen and the person who located it is less than 1 km. Probably many meteorites fall to Earth and pass unnoticed. This inefficiency in the collection of meteorites must be taken into account when we estimate the true number of objects that fall on the Earth.

Let N be the number of stone meteorites that fall on 1 km^2 of the Earth's surface during the period of 1 year. If the number N includes all meteorites with a mass equal to or greater than m kg, the rate is given by the expression

$$\text{Stone meteorites:} \qquad \log_{10}N = -3.73 - \log_{10}m \qquad \text{(7.1)}$$

The equation for iron meteorites is different:

$$\text{Irons:} \qquad \log_{10}N = -5.61 - 0.7\log_{10}m \qquad \text{(7.2)}$$

These equations have been derived from falls on the great plains in the United States and Europe, where most meteorites are recovered. For the whole Earth, Equations (7.1) and (7.2) predict that about 1,500 meteorites arrive during the course of a year with a mass greater than or equal to 100 kg. An object of mass 100 kg would be reduced to about 10 kg by the time it reached the ground, but the recovery rate of 10-kg meteorites is certainly not 1,500 per year. At the present time the collection rate is not much better than 5 or 10 per year, and the other 1,490 or so meteorites are lost to science. They land in the oceans, icefields, forests, and uninhabited deserts.

Meteorites are of great interest to astronomers, geochemists, and other scientists because they are a free sample of extraterrestrial material. Perhaps the term "free sample" is a little inappropriate, because the scientist must usually pay the finder at the rate of $10 per pound, or even more! Legislation has been proposed to define meteorites as property of the state. When this legislation is passed, meteorites will be handed over to the scientist without charge, except for the money and time spent in sleuthing.

Whether for monetary gain or for scientific advancement, it is well to have a look at any freshly disturbed areas in a field or desert to see whether a visitor from space may be resting just a few inches below the surface. If the object is iron, it is almost certainly a meteorite. If the object is stony, look for the following clues: the outside surface should be blackened—break a piece off, and small flakes of metal should be seen with the aid of a magnifying glass; it should be heavy, with a specific gravity of 3.5 g cm^{-3}. When in doubt take the specimen to a science museum or observatory. When an object is actually seen to fall or is found in a fresh crater following the appearance of a bright fireball in the sky, it is called a *fall*. When a meteorite is found by chance and it is not possible to tell exactly when it arrived, it is called a *find*. We are not as sure about the authenticity of a find as we are of a fall.

In the case of objects with a mass of a few kilograms, stones are more numerous than irons, the ratio being approximately 10:1. But in the case of meteorites with masses of the order of 10^{12} kg, irons are more numerous than stones. There is a difference in the size distribution of stony and iron meteorites; there are proportionately more small stony meteors than irons. This difference is of course shown by the coefficient for $\log_{10}m$ in Equations (7.1) and (7.2). A very simple explanation can be given for this difference. It is due to the collisions between meteorites in space. A similar phenomenon occurs on the Earth when ordinary rocks are crushed in the process of mineral dressing. The longer rock is crushed, the more small fragments are produced. Thus it is fair to conclude that the stones have suffered collisional damage in space to a greater extent than the irons. This is just what would be expected from consideration of the strength of materials. The crushing strength of the stone is considerably less than that of iron, and it is natural that the stony meteorites should suffer more damage as they smash together in space.

Meteorites with a mass less than 1 ton are slowed down to a considerable extent by the atmosphere. The meteorite approaches the Earth with an average velocity in the range 15 to 20 km sec^{-1}. The drag equation, Equation (2.1), gives the deceleration of the body as it penetrates into the atmosphere. By the time the meteorite has reached a height of 20 km, the initial velocity of approach has been reduced to 0, and the object falls freely, under the action of gravity, at its terminal velocity. This velocity, governed by the mass and size of the object, is usually about 0.1 km sec^{-1}, and so the meteorite makes a fairly soft landing.

If the original mass is 1,000 tons or more, the meteorite is not decelerated by the atmosphere to any appreciable extent. The change in velocity as derived from Equation (2.1) is trivial, because the column of atmosphere scooped out by the meteorite has much less mass than the meteorite itself. Under these conditions the meteorite strikes the surface of the Earth with its original cosmic velocity, and the effects are much more severe. Many craters scattered over the Earth's surface are attributed to the fall of large meteorites. The most famous is, perhaps, the meteorite crater near Winslow, Arizona. This crater has a maximum diameter of 1.2 km and a depth of 175 m, but was probably deeper when first formed, because the floor of the crater is now filled with silt and debris. Various estimates have been made to determine the mass of the object that formed this crater; the most frequently occurring figure is about 100,000 tons. Various estimates have also been made of its age, thought to be somewhere between 20,000 and 50,000 years old. In all probability there were nomadic tribes in the area at the time of the fall. The heat of the explosion and the cloud of debris would undoubtedly kill all life within 5 miles, and those further away would witness a terrifying sight. Indian folklore in the area does indeed allude to the event, and the stream bed nearby is called Canyon Diablo (Devil Canyon).

The Arizona crater is by no means the biggest on the surface of the Earth. Geologists have been carefully mapping surface features and making surveys for gravity anomalies, and have revealed some amazing "astroblemes," as they are called. Lake Bosumtwi in Ghana now fills a crater that was 10 km in diameter. The town of Nordlinger in Germany is set within a curved ridge of hills. Careful work has shown that the feature is an old crater, some 25 km in diameter. A similar ring of hills exists in South Africa where the geological strata have been bent upward and outward by a central force. This is known as the "Vredefort Ring"—the remains of a crater some 40 km in diameter. There is no doubt that the Earth's surface has been bombarded severely during the course of geological time, and this bombardment will undoubtedly continue in the future.

Although it is not possible to simulate such large-scale explosions on the surface of the Earth, it is possible to compute the motion of material and estimate the amount of damage that would be caused. R. L. Bjork has established equations which govern the movement of material during sudden impact conditions. A computing machine was programmed to follow through the explosion process for various sizes of impacting bodies. Calculations such as these give us our best estimate of the original mass of the Arizona meteorite. When the mass is about 5×10^{10} kg and the velocity of impact is 15 km sec^{-1}, the resulting crater is approximately 10 km in diameter. A dense plume of debris lifts off from the site of the explosion

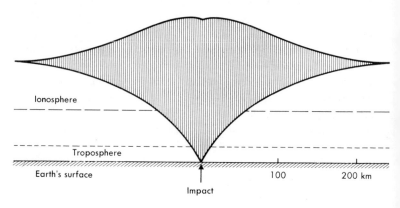

FIGURE 7.2   The plume over a meteorite crater.

and expands away from the crater. I have continued the work of Bjork to follow the path of material, using an IBM 7090 computer. In Figure 7.2 the shape and size of the plume is shown 60 seconds after impact. The density of the debris within the plume is at least 10 times the density of the surrounding atmosphere, so the expanding mushroom undoubtedly removes a portion of the atmosphere. Material is flung upward and outward for distances of hundreds and sometimes thousands of kilometers. Although this research is at the moment entirely academic, it would not be so if a similar event took place at some time in the future, and from Equation (7.2) this will occur several times in a million years!

In considering the nature of meteorites, the most important characteristic to note is the clear-cut division between iron and stony material. Seismographic study shows that the Earth is not composed of rock and stony material throughout its volume. There is a core some 4,300 miles in diameter that is in a molten condition. Furthermore, the specific gravity of the core is much higher than that of rock, being close to the value for molten iron. These and other factors lead us to suppose that the Earth has in its interior a core of liquid iron which is surrounded by a mantle of solid rock some 2,000 miles thick. It is quite natural to suppose that the iron meteorites are material from the core of a planet, and that stony meteorites are from the surrounding mantle.

At this point we must take account of the astronomical evidence. Between the orbits of Mars and Jupiter a large number of small planets have been found, known collectively as the asteroids. Ceres is the largest of them, with a diameter of 480 miles, but the average asteroid detected is no more than a few miles across. Ceres appears as a very tiny disk in the most powerful telescopes, but most of the other asteroids show evidence for irregular shapes. The reflected light varies rapidly from hour to hour, which is consistent with the rapid spinning of an irregular object. Also, the asteroid Eros was seen through powerful telescopes to be an irregular brick-shaped object when it passed close by the Earth. A few of the asteroids have long elliptical orbits and pass close to the Earth's orbit as they move around the sun. Thus, from the astronomical evidence, it is reasonable to suppose that meteorites are indeed asteroids that have been deflected from the asteroid zone between Mars and Jupiter, also that the asteroids themselves are fragments of a former planet.

It has been suggested that the asteroids were formed almost as they are at present—a swarm of irregular fragments. This is unlikely, because it is difficult to explain how the iron could be separated out so efficiently by such a process. There are other factors to be discussed later, such as Widmanstätten figures, that argue against the formation of meteorites and asteroids as individual objects. It has also been suggested that the asteroids were formed by the breakup of a single original planet, but this suggestion is not easy to support because of the very great amount of energy required to explode a planet.

A generally accepted theory is that two or more small planets, perhaps something like Ceres, were formed in the asteroid zone and suffered a collision. The relative velocity during the collision would probably be between 5 and 10 km sec^{-1} if the planetoids had orbits similar to the asteroids at present. This velocity is sufficient to break up the colliding bodies and scatter the material. The original planets were probably very similar to Ceres in size, the size being fixed to within fairly narrow limits by considerations of the heating and subsequent cooling of the original planet. Firstly, the planet must be of sufficient size for the interior to become heated in the beginning by radioactivity and for chemical separation of iron and silica to take place. Secondly, the planet must be somewhat smaller than the moon, because calculations have shown that if an object the size of the moon became molten in the interior, there has not been sufficient time in the history of the solar system for the object to cool down and solidify. Yet iron meteorites show crystal patterns and were undoubtedly formed from a solid iron core and not a liquid core. Thus the original planet was probably about 1,000 km in diameter, which is sufficient in size for a core to form during the early stages in the life of the planet yet is not too large to prevent cooling by radiation and the solidification of the core.

When stony meteorites are studied in detail, it is possible to divide them into subclasses. The first and most important division is between the *chondrites* and the *achondrites.* Eighty-five per cent of all witnessed meteorite falls have been chondrites; of the 1,018 stone falls, 954 were chondrites, nearly 95 per cent. Thus chondrites are the most prevalent type of meteorite in space.

Nearly 50 different minerals have been identified in meteorites, but the bulk of a meteorite is generally composed of a few major constituents. The chondrites are composed of olivine, pyroxene, oligoclase, troilite, and flecks of nickel-iron. Apart from the metallic nickel-iron, these minerals are well known to terrestrial geologists. When viewed through a microscope a thin section of a chondrite shows these minerals in a disorderly array, quite unlike any terrestrial rock, with the fragments no more than a fraction of a millimeter across. The distinguishing feature of a meteorite is the *chondrule,* a round inclusion from which the chondrite takes its name; that shown in Figure 7.3 is approximately 1 mm in diameter and is a typical example. Chondrules usually consist of olivine and/or orthopyroxene, and a prismatic crystal structure usually radiates from a point that is not at the center of the chondrule. The density of chondrites is somewhat higher than that of terrestrial rock because of the inclusion of flecks of nickel-iron amounting to 15 per cent by weight.

The *carbonaceous chondrites* form an interesting subgroup. These meteorites are extremely rare, forming not more than 2 per cent of the total sample of stones, but they are of great interest because of their unusual mineralogical and chemical composition. These chondrites are very dark in color throughout because of the inclusion of about 5 per cent of black, tarlike material presumed to be a complex polymer of high molecular weight. An organic chemist would undoubtedly define the chemical as "organic," but there is much dispute as to whether these polymers have actually been formed by living organisms. It is possible for such compounds of carbon, hydrogen, and oxygen to be formed by completely dead, inorganic processes.

The carbonaceous chondrites are fragile and porous and have a low density of approximately 2.2 g cm^{-3}. The low crushing strength may be responsible in part for their scarcity. Perhaps more of these objects enter the Earth's atmosphere but do not survive the entry; the porous structure may also account for the discovery of microscopic structures within the meteorite. At first these structures were considered to be cosmic fossils, but later work shows that they are probably terrestrial spores that have seeped into the specimen.

The *achondrites,* as the name implies, do not contain chondrules. The most common minerals found in this group are pyroxene and plagioclase. The texture is more coarse and does not present such a jumbled appearance as the chondrites. Flakes of nickel-iron are entirely absent or very rare in these specimens; in fact, they are very similar to terrestrial rocks and have been likened to gabbro.

Because of the similarity to terrestrial rocks, achondrites are very difficult to find, and many may pass unnoticed. The only achondrites that can be positively identified are the few examples that have been observed to fall. The percentage of achondrites in space can be estimated from the statistics of witnessed falls; approximately 5 per cent of the stony meteorites are achondrites.

The chondrule is regarded by many scientists as primordial material. That is to say, it represents a small particle that has condensed from gases at the time the solar system was formed. These particles then collected together under the action of gravity to form the texture of the chondritic meteorite. The flecks of nickel-iron may represent primordial particles or, less probably, splinters from smashed iron meteorites. Ordinary chondrites are thought to have undergone more pressure and heating than carbonaceous chondrites. Perhaps the latter were originally located near the surface of the asteroids before the collision occurred.

The achondrites, on the other hand, are considered to show the effects of change, or metamorphism, and are thought to have crystallized from a magma in the same way that terrestrial rocks were produced. The achondrites could therefore be derived from chondritic material that has been melted and subsequently re-crystallized; the fact that they represent only a small percentage of the material adds substance to this hypothesis.

The nickel-iron meteorites make a very interesting set, because it is easy to visualize how all the different classes could form from a single original mixture; they probably crystallized very slowly in the molten core of a small planet. Indeed, from the evidence presented by the various groups of iron meteorites, it is very difficult to see how the irons could have formed in any other way. If all the irons are averaged together, the average nickel content is approximately 9 per cent by weight. The overall ratio in the universe of iron to nickel is approximately 17:1. Thus the proportion of nickel in iron meteorites is in agreement with the cosmic mix, the extra 3 per cent of nickel in the iron meteorites being attributable to the affinity of nickel and iron and a chemical differentiation process. The iron and nickel, of course, could only separate and sink into the core of the planet if the temperature rose sufficiently to melt the materials.

Let us suppose that the core cools and crystallizes. Metallurgists have studied the properties of a nickel-iron mixture in great detail. There are two processes that can take place—first a crystal can grow within the melt, then slow changes can take place in the solid crystal as it cools. Iron with a low nickel content crystallizes at a high temperature, and so a nickel-iron mineral (*taenite*) is the first to form within the melt. As the temperature falls, this mineral transforms to *kamacite,* which is a body-centered cubic crystal with a nickel content between the narrow limits of 5 to 6 per cent. Since there are atoms at each corner of a cube, the shape of the crystal is a hexahedron, a six-sided figure. This mineral is represented among the iron meteorites by the *hexahedrites.*

When a hexahedrite is sliced and the surface is polished and etched with a dilute acid, the planes of the crystal lattice show up as faint lines. If the slice is taken parallel to one face of the cube, the lines are in two mutually perpendicular directions (see Figure 7.4). In the Bennett County meteorite the lattice lines are somewhat obscured by an additional set of lines known as "Neumann bands," caused by a slippage of the crystal structure, like a sliding pack of cards. Neumann bands are found in all hexahedrites and are most readily produced when the crystal is subjected to a violent impact between the temperatures of 300 and 600°C. The bands were probably produced when the solidified core of the small planet was smashed by encounter with another body.

A careful look at the surface of the Bennett County meteorite will show that the crystal lattice extends all over the face. Thus the meteorite is a single, almost perfect, crystal. In general the crystals in hexahedrites are several inches across, which indicates good annealing. Under laboratory conditions it is difficult to grow large crystals from a cooling liquid, and the giant hexahedrite crystals indicate that the crystallization process took place over a long period of time in a quiet environment. Presumably the nickel-iron core of the small planet required several million years to solidify.

As the kamacite crystals formed, the mother liquid became richer in its nickel content. It is known that crystals of taenite again form when the nickel content is greater than 6 per cent, but nickel-rich taenite does not degenerate during the annealing process. Taenite forms in octahedral (eight-sided) crystals. The octahedron has the shape of two square pyramids set base to base, and the atoms can be visualized as set in the center of the six faces of a cube. The mineral taenite is the basic constituent of an *octahedrite,* which is the most prevalent type of iron meteorite.

The typical polished and etched surface of an octahedrite is shown in Figure 7.5. This sample has been cut parallel to one face of the octahedron. Since each face of the octahedron is triangular, the lines in the crystal cover the surface of the specimen in three different directions. In a perfect crystal the lattice lines would not show so markedly as they do in Figure 7.5. The remarkable pattern of octahedrites is called the "Widmanstätten pattern" and is caused by a minor degenerative process in the octahedral crystal during the annealing process. The bands are poor in nickel—in fact they are kamacite. Over a long period of time the nickel atoms have diffused away from the bands and have moved into the nickel-rich areas. The original structure of the taenite crystal, however, is not affected by this diffusion, and the partial separation of the nickel conveniently shows us the original structure.

The octahedral crystal does not slip so easily under impact as the hexahedron. Neumann bands have never been seen in the taenite portion of octahedrites, but they are noticeable when the kamacite of the Widmanstätten pattern is closely examined. Thus the octahedrites, like the hexahedrites, have certainly been subjected to a violent shock during their history.

As crystallization proceeded in the core, the mother liquid would be further enriched in nickel. When the nickel content reached about 25 per cent, the octahedral crystals of taenite would form as before. But with the high percentage of nickel, no degeneration would take place in the solid crystal as it annealed, which accounts for the nickel-rich *ataxites*. Approximately one iron meteorite in a hundred contains more than 25 per cent nickel, and then the inclusions of kamacite are very rare, if not entirely absent.

What is the maximum content of nickel that might be expected? In the laboratory, the melting point of a nickel-iron alloy becomes lower as more nickel is added. The lowest melting point occurs at 1430°C at normal atmospheric pressure when the nickel content is 68 per cent. This means that the mother liquid of the nickel-iron core would be expected to solidify as a whole when the nickel content reached 68 per cent. The maximum nickel content observed so far was found in the Oktibbeha County, Mississippi, meteorite, in which the nickel content was 62 per cent. This is a remarkable confirmation of the hypothesis that all nickel-iron meteorites were formed by solidification from a nickel-iron melt in the core of a small planet.

scale height of the atmosphere is H cm and that the air density is ρ at a height h. The mass per unit area in the column of atmosphere above h is ρH. Meteors with a velocity of 30 km sec^{-1} begin to ablate at $h = 100$ km, where $\rho \simeq 1.4 \times 10^{-9}$ g cm^{-3} and $H = 7.0 \times 10^5$ cm. Thus if an object has a mass per unit area $\leqq 10^{-3}$ g cm^{-2}, it will be decelerated before ablation begins and will become a micrometeorite. For a spherical particle with radius r and density 3 g cm^{-3} it is easy to show that the mass per unit area is $4r$ g cm^{-2}. Thus when $r \leqq 2.5 \times 10^{-4}$ cm, the particle is a micrometeorite. For micrometeorites with a very slow cosmic velocity, r is somewhat larger, and if partial melting takes place, the critical radius is also larger.

According to Equation (5.4), micrometeorites should be quite plentiful; at a radius of 2.4 μ or greater we can expect several micrometeorites to fall each day on 1 cm^2 of surface. How can we collect them? Sticky plates have been exposed and the catch examined with a microscope, but the plates pick up so much industrial soot and other forms of contamination that positive identification of visitors from space is almost hopeless. In clean air on mountain tops the sticky plates do pick up particles at the rate of 1 cm^{-2} day^{-1} with $r \geqq 10$ μ. This rate is close to the expected value, and these particles may be true micrometeorites.

Sticky plates and collection filters have been flown in U-2 planes at great altitudes. Although many particles are collected, there is still some doubt as to whether they are really of extraterrestrial origin. Some at least have proved to be chrome-steel and are probably small flakes from an aircraft engine! Other particles are similar to terrestrial dust and may have been blown into the atmosphere by active volcanoes.

To avoid these uncertainties, scientists decided to "go up and get them." Collecting boxes were placed in the nose cones of rockets, opened in the high atmosphere, and returned to Earth by parachute. Different types of collecting surfaces are used—some are made from hard plastic, some are thin mylar films, and some are metal. The catch is examined by all available techniques. A high-power electron microscope is used to find the particles and study their form; electron diffraction shows the possible crystal structures;

and X-ray fluorescence reveals the various elements that are present.

Of all the millions of micrometeorites captured by rockets, three typical ones are shown in Figures 7.6 to 7.8. The first is a loose collection of very small particles forming an open network and is recognized as a typical cometary meteor, fragile and of low effective density. It is a remarkable confirmation of the "fluffy" model derived indirectly from photographic and radio observations. The particle in Figure 7.7 is more compact and probably of higher density and strength. It is not a solid chip of rock, because it is semitransparent in the electron microscope and shows many inclusions. Micrometeorites of this type are probably related to the loose aggregates and may perhaps be formed from them by a compacting process.

The third type, Figure 7.8, is almost spherical and probably represents a fast and/or dense particle that has been melted during the deceleration process. Notice the evidence for a low impact velocity, consistent with the micrometeorite theory. The particle disturbed the mylar film but did not penetrate it completely; it was stopped like an acrobat dropping onto a sticky trampoline.

Some micrometeorites show a crystal structure, but most of them do not. This is quite surprising. Almost all dust particles and mineral fragments on the Earth show a crystal structure, no matter how finely the material is divided. The reason for this anomaly shown by extraterrestrial particles is not known at the time of writing. Micrometeorites are certainly heated during the collision with the atmosphere, but their form usually does not show any sign of melting. It is therefore unlikely that any original crystals have been destroyed by rapid heating and cooling. If each micrometeorite contained hundreds of fragments of different minerals, the crystal patterns would not show up with electron diffraction; but this would mean that almost all the tiny fragments that make a single micrometeorite, such as the fluffy object in Figure 7.6, were different minerals, and this is unlikely. There is the possibility that dust particles formed within a cometary nucleus are indeed without crystalline form. If the material has collected together in a cold environment, there may not have been sufficient energy to place the atoms in the definite positions of a crystal structure.

Small meteoroids have received a great deal of attention recently because they are a hazard to space travel. The velocity of the object is sufficiently great to puncture the skin of a spacecraft, and even the impact of many extremely small nonpenetrating particles can erode the surface and cause a window to become frosted and useless. Attempts have been made to estimate the effects of space damage. The number of meteors striking the spacecraft can be determined approximately from the flux observed by observers on the surface of the Earth, and the damage can be estimated from the physical theory. Uncertainties seem to exist in the theory, and a more recent approach has been to fly a spacecraft with the intended purpose of inflicting damage. Metal cans of various thicknesses have been orbited and the number of punctures counted. General results show that although meteoroids do present a space hazard, they will not prevent the progress of national space programs.

※ **8** ※

comets
and
their
orbits

We normally think of a comet as a spectacular object, striking fear into the hearts of men. Certainly in the past some comets have made an outstanding sight, shining as brightly as the planet Venus and displaying a long, eerie tail. In 1910, for instance, Halley's Comet showed a tail that was more than 100 deg long and stretched across the sky from horizon to horizon. But not all comets are spectacular; in fact, the vast majority are insignificant, fuzzy specks of light. Most of the comets that visit the sun each year never become visible to the unaided eye and must be examined with powerful telescopes and cameras. Most comets when discovered are close to the limit of detection, magnitude +10, +15, or even as faint as +20.

A comet is named after the person who discovers it, and a maximum of three independent discoverers are recognized. This honor has no doubt attracted many people to the ranks of "comet hunters," and until recently most of the comets known to science were discovered by amateurs. Professional astronomers have contributed to the discoveries, but usually in an accidental fashion. They have found comets on photographic plates primarily exposed for photographing stars or searching for asteroids. In Czechoslovakia a very successful search for comets has been carried out for more than 5 years at the Skalnaté Pleso Observatory. Visual observers were employed to search the sky with high-power binoculars (25 × 100 mm).

Searching for a comet is a very exacting task. There are millions of faint stars that must be passed over each night during the search. A comet will show as a small hazy disk and will not focus as sharply as a star. Even so, there are many objects to mislead the comet hunter. At the time of discovery a comet is too far away from the sun to develop the characteristic tail. Distant galaxies, emission nebulas, and unresolved star clusters are all very much like a comet in appearance. The only sure way of identifying a suspected object is to observe it on subsequent nights. A comet will reveal itself by moving against the star background, whereas nebulas and more distant objects will not show movement.

As a comet approaches the sun, it grows brighter. A solid object approaching the sun would change in brightness according to the inverse square law, i.e., the brightness would vary as $(distance)^{-2}$. The average comet, however, shows a more rapid change in brightness, and the exponent is usually between -4 and -6. The illumination falling on the comet from the sun is of course still governed by the inverse square law. The excess of brightness is due to a change in the size of the comet, and the hazy outline is caused by a cloud of gas continuously escaping from the nucleus of the comet, the *coma*. As a comet approaches the sun, the escape of gas increases, and the coma grows in size and brightness.

A very bright comet will show a *nucleus*, which appears as a small starlike point of light in the center of the coma. The fainter comets do not show a nucleus, but it is reasonable to suppose that a nucleus is present and could be observed if a more powerful telescope were available. The nucleus changes in brightness as the comet approaches the sun, but the change is less pronounced than the change in brightness of the coma. A spectrum of the light from the nucleus shows the typical spectrum of sunlight, a bright continuum crossed by many dark Fraunhofer absorption lines. These and other observations show that a comet has at its center a small solid object from which, presumably, the gases of the coma are generated under the heating action of the sun. The diameter of the nucleus is difficult to measure, but estimates indicate a diameter of a few miles for the larger comets. The coma, on the other hand, is very much larger than the nucleus. The gases spread out for several hundred thousand miles.

The nucleus reflects sunlight directly; there is no appreciable change in wavelength. The coma shines by fluorescence, a process in which light is absorbed at one wavelength and reemitted at another. Atoms and molecules in the gas are responsible for this phenomenon. Light of short wavelength is absorbed by the atom, which is raised to an excited state. When the atom returns to its normal energy state, light is reemitted, usually at a longer wavelength than the light that caused the excitation. Each atom and molecule fluoresces with particular colors or with particular wavelengths and can therefore be identified from its emission spectrum. The most conspicuous lines are from the molecule CN, a combination of carbon and nitrogen. Cyanogen, a poisonous gas, has the formula C_2N_2, and so CN can be regarded as one-half of a cyanogen molecule. CN is a free radical, and any appreciable concentration of this material would react explosively to form cyanogen gas. In the coma, the density of the gas is very low, and no reaction can take place. Other molecules are found, composed of the atoms of nitrogen, carbon, oxygen, and hydrogen: NH and NH_2, free radicals of ammonia; CH, a free radical of methane; and OH, the hydroxyl group. Swan bands are very conspicuous in the spectrum of the coma, and these bands are produced by the carbon molecule C_2. Evidence has also been found for the carbon molecule C_3.

The tail is the most characteristic feature of a typical comet, and that of Mrkos is a fine example (see Figure 8.1). The tail points away from the sun at all times, even when the comet has passed perihelion and is moving away from the sun, in which case it is moving tail first. To be exact we must recognize two types of tails, curved and straight, and both types point away from the sun because of some type of repulsive force.

The curved tail does not show pronounced emission lines in the spectrum and is therefore not made of gas. It is composed of finely divided solid particles—comet dust. The particles must have been released from the nucleus and then blown into the tail, but how? Calculations show that light exerts a very small pressure when it falls upon an object. The pressure of sunlight is sufficiently strong to separate the dust particles from the parent comet and cause them to be scattered in a curved path which forms the tail.

The straight tail is quite different. It points directly away from the sun and is much narrower than the dust tail. The spectrum contains bright emission lines characteristic of a fluorescing gas. Whereas the atoms of molecules in the coma are electrically neutral, the molecules in the tail are ionized. The molecule has lost an electron and becomes positively charged. The most conspicuous lines from the tail are produced by carbon monoxide; in addition carbon dioxide, nitrogen, and ionized free radicals have been observed. The tail of ionized gas is straight because the repulsive force is very strong. Puffs of gas have been observed moving along the tail at speeds of several hundred kilometers per second. It is not possible for light pressure to produce such violent effects, and the reason for them is not known at the time of writing. It has been suggested that the ionized tail is a gaseous plasma and is interacting with charged particles emitted from the sun.

A comet changes in appearance from night to night, and no comet can be identified from its shape alone. The only sure identification is the orbit in which the comet moves, because we very seldom find new comets moving along the same path. In fact we can discuss comets in general in terms of their orbits, dividing them into two well-defined classes, the *short-period* comets and the *long-period* comets. The dividing line between the groups is somewhat arbitrarily set at a period of 200 years.

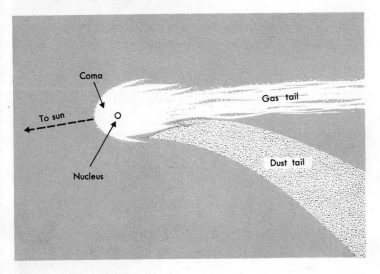

FIGURE 8.2   The anatomy of a comet.

If a comet returns to perihelion once every 200 years or less, it belongs to the short-period group. Most of the members of the group, however, have a much shorter period of 6 years, and the average is 20 years. Since the beginning of observational astronomy 566 comets have been well observed and their orbits computed. Of these 94, or approximately 20 per cent, fall in the short-period class.

Short-period comets form a well-ordered group. With the exception of seven, they all move in direct orbits following the general motion of the planets around the sun. The inclination of the plane of the orbit to the plane of the solar system is usually small, about 15 deg. The typical orbit is an ellipse with the moderate eccentricity of 0.5 and an aphelion of 5 AU, which is the distance of the planet Jupiter from the sun. Several meteor swarms follow the orbits of short-period comets, and probably all the major meteor streams are related to this group.

Approximately 80 per cent of the sample (472) are long-period comets. To the first approximation the orbit is a parabola with an infinite period. It is very difficult to calculate the elements of the orbit for these comets, since a slight perturbation from a planet will turn a parabolic orbit into a long ellipse or a hyperbola. Small unavoidable errors in observing the position of the comet will also introduce uncertainties in the calculated orbit. A few gaps in the observations due to clouds and other troubles can easily result in a hyperbolic orbit being calculated when the true orbit is a long ellipse. Faced with these observational and mathematical difficulties, it is not generally possible to do better than assume that the orbit is exactly a parabola. In fact, no fewer than 290 orbits of long-period comets are given as parabolas, even though it is well known that a parabolic orbit is a singular condition which probably never occurs in reality. To examine long-period comets in more detail, it is essential to look very closely at subgroups where the observations were good and no trouble was spared in the mathematical calculations.

Definite elliptical orbits are shown by 117 long-period comets. The eccentricity is very large, ranging from 0.963 to 0.999995. The periods range from 250 years to 30 million years. One-half of the group have periods greater than 6,000 years. These results are the best that can be obtained from existing data, and all that can be concluded is that these comets have very long periods with an average value of perhaps a million years. Clearly our lifetime is too short to observe these comets on a second visit to the sun, and we have no way of improving the data.

At least 65 long-period comets have eccentricities greater than 1.0, that is to say, their orbits are hyperbolic. As we have seen in Chapter 5, a hyperbolic orbit opens up the interesting possibility of interstellar traffic. Do these comets come to the sun from neighboring stars? The answer is "No." Careful calculations have shown that these comets move in very long closed ellipses when outside the orbit of Jupiter. At great distances from the solar system, the comet is moving under the combined action of the sun and Jupiter, the largest planet. When the comet is near the sun at perihelion, the gravitational field is that of the sun alone. Thus at perihelion

the orbit is slightly hyperbolic, but at aphelion it is slightly elliptical. Astronomers conclude that no truly hyperbolic comet has yet
been observed and that these comets are really moving around the
sun in closed orbits.

It goes without saying that the 290 parabolic orbits would fit
into either the long-period class or the hyperbolic class if more
accurate observations were available. Thus we have to conclude
that all long-period comets are members of the solar system with
very long periods, probably measured in millions of years. They do
not form a well-ordered group like the short-period comets, and
their orbits are tilted in all directions to the plane of the solar
system. There are 227 directly moving comets and 245 in retrograde orbits. The fact that these numbers are almost equal indicates that the orbits of long-period comets are tilted at random and
bear no relation to the plane in which the planets move. There may
be some significance in the slightly smaller number of directly
moving orbits, and this will be discussed in the next chapter.

Out of the hundreds of comets, a few have become quite famous;
most are unusual in some respect and must not be regarded as
typical of the average comet. Halley's Comet is well known because
it is large and passes near the Earth's orbit at fairly regular intervals. Sir Edmund Halley never saw the comet that bears his
name, but he deserves the honor of patronymesis nevertheless.
Using celestial mechanics, which had just been developed by his
friend, Sir Isaac Newton, he computed the orbit of several comets.
He noticed that the bright comets of 1531, 1607, and 1682 were
separated by an interval of about 75 years and that the orbits were
very similar. He argued that this indicated the existence of one
object making periodic returns to the sun. Halley predicted that
the comet would return in late 1758 or early 1759, and it was first
sighted on Christmas Day, 1758. Comets were thus shown to be
members of the solar system amenable to the laws of physics, with
no supernatural power of motion. Cometary astronomy had begun.

The last perihelion passage of Halley's Comet was in 1910, when
it was a spectacular object in the late spring. A rare event hap-
pened at this return—the comet passed directly between the Earth
and the sun. When Mercury and Venus do so, they are seen sil-

houetted against the bright disk of the sun, but Halley's Comet could not be seen at all under these conditions, confirming that the coma was a semitransparent gas and that the nucleus was of no great size. At this time the tail of the comet stretched away from the sun for millions of miles, and the planet Earth must have passed through some portion of the tail. There were of course no noticeable effects, since the gaseous tail is very rarefied, less than 10^{-20} g cm^{-3}. In 1948 Halley's Comet reached aphelion between the orbits of Neptune and Pluto and began its long journey back to the sun. It will be near the Earth again in 1986.

The period of Halley's Comet is more than 10 times greater than that of a typical short-period comet. Encke is a comet with an exceptionally short period. It returns to the sun every 3.3 years and has one of the shortest periods known. The comet was discovered in 1786 and in 1964 visited the sun for the 55th time. It has been observed on every return since 1822 and has become a regular feature on the astronomical calendar. Encke is a comet without a tail; the coma develops in the warmth of sunlight, but the quantity of gas and fine dust is small when compared with other comets. The amount of dust and gas expelled from a comet near perihelion is considerable, and a comet must ultimately be destroyed by this process. It is not known for how many revolutions a comet can survive, but the number is probably between 100 and 1,000. Encke is undoubtedly formed by the remnants of a once larger comet which probably grew many splendid tails in the past. In its present state, the comet is thought to be protected by a layer of dust which envelops the nucleus and slows down the evaporation process.

Encke posed quite a problem to the celestial mechanicians of the nineteenth century. Accurate observations showed that the period was decreasing by about 2½ hours each revolution. What was the cause? It was conjectured that there was a "resisting medium" in space which caused the comet to spiral in toward the sun in the same way that our modern artificial satellites meet the resistance of the atmosphere and return to earth. But the effect was not so noticeable with other comets, and why should Encke be so different? The explanation that replaced the idea of a resisting medium and finally gained acceptance was based upon the "rocket effect." Gases leak out from cracks in the dust shell around the nucleus, and these jets impart a backward thrust on the nucleus, causing the comet to move in an orbit of decreasing size.

Oterma is a comet that tried to become an asteroid. In the 1930s this comet moved in an almost circular orbit beyond the planet Jupiter. The comet was in the neighborhood of Jupiter for the 3 years between 1936 and 1939 and suffered a severe perturbation from that planet. As a result the period of the comet was changed from 18 years to 7.9 years, and the new orbit was in the asteroid zone. The inclination was 4 deg, the distance from the sun at perihelion was 3.5 AU, and the aphelion distance was 4.4 AU. With this orbit, Oterma would certainly have passed the selection tests and been classified as an asteroid if other factors had not given it away. Even though it was so far from the sun, the comet continued to show a gaseous coma, which is the most important identification mark of a comet.

Between 1962 and 1964 the comet was scheduled to make another close encounter with Jupiter, and it did. It passed within 0.1 AU of the planet, which is quite close, and suffered another perturbation. The orbit was once again entirely outside the orbit of Jupiter, and the comet is now much farther from the sun and the Earth. Astronomers will be lucky if they can keep track of the object in its new orbit, because it is very faint and is not expected to become brighter than magnitude +20. Of course there is always the hope that it will suffer a perturbation in the future and will be brought once again into a region of accessibility.

Comet Brooks is another example of a Jupiter perturbation. In 1886 it was within 0.01 AU of Jupiter, passing between the Jovian satellites. Before the encounter the period was 29 years; after the encounter it was reduced to 7.1 years. This encounter, incidentally, gave proof that the nucleus of the comet must be held together by cohesive forces. An object whose distance from a planet is less than 2.5 times the radius of the planet is within the Roche limit. The gravitational field of the planet will raise tidal disturbances in the object, and if the object has no cohesive strength, it will be scattered into a multitude of fragments. Comet Brooks did not disintegrate, and thus the nucleus must have a certain amount of cohesive strength.

A few comets have been observed to break up, presumably because the nucleus split into two or more portions. Comet Biela is perhaps the best example. In 1846 this comet had become double, and the two objects began to separate very slowly. When the double comet returned to the sun in 1852, the two nuclei were separated by over a million miles, and each had developed a normal coma and tail. The twins separated from each other at a rate of a few kilometers per hour, which is a fairly slow speed astronomically speaking. They were never seen again after the return of 1852.

The original nucleus had probably broken in half under the action of gas pressure or other forces. The heating action of the sun continued to evaporate the ices, and the disappearance of the comets indicates that the nuclei were very quickly degassed. As explained in Chapter 4, the solid particles from the original comets continued to move in an orbit around the sun. When the Earth passed through the orbit of the defunct comet in 1872, a brilliant display of shooting stars was seen. Observations of the meteor swarm showed that the particles had not strayed far from the original position of the comet. Indeed, the rate of separation of the meteor particles from the comet was no more than a few kilometers per second, the same order of magnitude as the velocity of separation of the two nuclei.

Other comets have been seen with a double nucleus. Comet Liais in 1860 and Comet Taylor in 1916 showed a double nucleus. In 1957 Comet Wirtanen was double, and the two components steadily increased their separation. From the rate of separation, it was deduced that Wirtanen must have split in two at a distance of at least 4.5 AU from the sun. The effects of solar radiation at this distance would be negligible, and some internal force may have split the nucleus.

Perhaps the most interesting example of the disruption of comets is the phenomenon of comet groups. A comet in a parabolic orbit must have a very long period, but sometimes two or more comets are seen in the same parabolic orbit within an interval of a few years. This can only mean that two or more comets are moving in the same parabolic orbit. These are known as comet groups, and at least 15 have been observed.

The biggest and best-known group is composed of the five sun-grazing comets. The great comet of 1882 came toward the sun in a parabolic orbit and passed within 7×10^5 miles of the photosphere. Calculations show that the comet must have passed around the sun in just a few hours, and during that time it was embedded in the sun's corona. Of course observations were not possible during the encounter because of the glare of the sun. Later observations showed that the comet had survived the encounter, but there were some strange symptoms. A bright filament was observed to come from the coma for a short while, and also some "beads" were seen in the vicinity of the head. No doubt portions of the nucleus had been broken away during this unusually close approach to the sun.

Although the period of Comet 1882 II was nearly 1,000 years, the orbit was the same as Comet 1843 I and Comet 1880 I. Later another sun-grazing comet was seen in 1887, and the final one in the series came by in 1945. There can be no doubt that these five comets are related and must have a common origin. Presumably a parent comet on a previous passage through the sun's corona was disrupted into at least five fragments, each of which formed a separate nucleus capable of forming a coma and tail. The period of the parent comet was no doubt of the order of 1,000 years, yet the separation of the five fragments did not proceed rapidly because on subsequent returns three of them came by the sun in an interval of less than 10 years. If the velocity of separation were of the order of a few kilometers per second, then the five fragments could return to the sun again within a time span of about 100 years.

It is clear from the observations of comets that the nucleus does have a certain amount of cohesive strength, for Comet Brooks was not disrupted when it passed close to the planet Jupiter. Also the sun-grazing comets between 1843 and 1945 have survived the great tidal strain produced by a close encounter with the sun. On the other hand, the nucleus is not strong enough to resist breakup completely. The very existence of comet groups shows that some comet in the past has yielded to the tidal strain, and the observations of Biela and other double comets show that the nucleus can sometimes split in two of its own accord. The physical nature of an object that can do this and produce such copious amounts of gas and dust must be explained by any successful model for a comet, and this subject will be taken up in the next chapter.

**the
nature
and origin
of comets**

When their general properties are considered, all comets are found to behave according to a single pattern. In deducing their nature, therefore, a single theory is sought that can explain the physical phenomena of comets, rather than two or more different theories. All comets show a coma in the vicinity of the sun, and most comets develop a tail. The usual spectrum of the coma and tail is a continuum with superimposed emission lines. The continuum indicates reflection from solid particles, and in fact from the reddening of the reflected light the diameter of the particles is determined to be of the order of 1 μ. Since finely divided ice particles would evaporate in the heat of the sun, these particles must be nonvolatile solids in the form of dust. A meteor swarm or stream moving in the orbit of a comet is further proof that these objects scatter solid debris along their track. Gases in the coma and tail appear as the comet nears the sun; these gases must evaporate from volatile solids. Thus there is no doubt that a comet contains solid particles of various sizes and substances from which gases can be derived under the action of heat.

One of the earliest theories described a comet as a compact swarm of meteors, similar to a flying gravel bank. This theory has been proved wrong, and it is interesting to follow the arguments that have led to its downfall.

The ratio of dust to gas in a typical comet is 1000:1. The total mass of Halley's Comet is estimated to be 10^{19} g, and the gas lost through the tail during each perihelion passage is 10^{14} g. Thus in 100 returns to the sun, 0.1 per cent of the mass has been evaporated and lost to the comet. There can be no hope for this gas to join the comet again at aphelion, because it is blown from the solar system in strongly hyperbolic orbits.

Now 0.1 per cent of the mass of a comet is a great deal of gas. If the solids in the comets formed a compact ball a few kilometers in diameter, the frozen gases would be several meters thick on the surface. The model we are dealing with, however, is a compact swarm of particles, and in this case it is possible to say that the gas is adsorbed on the surfaces. The smaller the particle, the greater the percentage of adsorbed gases. Calculations show that the particles must be of the order of a few microns in diameter so as to adsorb 0.1 per cent. But particles no more than a few microns in diameter are an impossibility; the light pressure from the sun is very strong for small particles and would greatly disturb the orbit of the comet. As has been shown in connection with comet tails, this repulsion can become so strong as to blow small particles away from the head of the comet. Comets would not obey Kepler's laws of orbital motion if the bulk of the comet were composed of fine particles.

A swarm of independent particles could not survive gravitational disturbances. We have seen how a meteor swarm becomes spread entirely around the orbit as some particles move ahead and others lag behind. A swarm of particles is very frequently subjected to a disturbing force as it passes between the planets on its journey around the sun. The force on one part of the swarm must inevitably be slightly different from the force on another part, and the particles will become separated. A comet might be expected to become gradually elongated with time, as the particles became spread around the orbit, yet comets remain as discrete, localized objects for hundreds of years. Encke, with its small round coma, has made more than 50 returns to the sun. Halley has been observed over a time span longer than 2,000 years and still shows a discrete, starlike nucleus.

Dispersion of a swarm becomes even more serious when the comet passes close to an object, such as the five sun-grazing comets and the passage of Comet Brooks between the satellites of Jupiter in 1886. Yet Comet Brooks exists today, and although the sun-grazing comets may have divided into several fragments, they did not become completely dispersed as a loose swarm would have done.

Finally, the nucleus is incontrovertible evidence that a comet is more than a swarm of particles. Admittedly not all comets have shown a nucleus, but it is difficult to observe owing to its small size. The nucleus of Halley's Comet shines in reflected sunlight as a starlike point of light. We can estimate its size from its brightness, if the albedo (reflecting power) is known. Assuming that about 10 per cent of the light is reflected, which is a reasonable figure, the diameter of the nucleus is 20 km. Assuming a density of 1 g cm^{-3}, the mass of the nucleus is 10^{19} g. This is very close to the total mass of dust and gas that Comet Halley is expected to lose during the course of its history. The mass loss is determined from the amount observable in the tail at each return and the mass of debris scattered around the orbit in the form of a meteor stream. Thus it is reasonable to suppose that the nucleus is a compact solid chunk responsible for all cometary phenomena. It provides the gas and dust for the coma and tail, and also the particles of a meteor stream. It has cohesive strength and can withstand the disruptive forces produced by a close encounter with the sun or a planet.

The "flying gravel bank" has been replaced by the "icy conglomerate" model, and a comet is sometimes referred to as a "dirty iceberg," but the term may be somewhat misleading. The exact proportion of solids and ices is not known, but it is quite probable that the amount of solid is greater than the amount of ice. Under these conditions the nucleus would resemble a frozen mass of soil or dust rather than a dirty iceberg.

It is possible to imagine what the nucleus must look like from our observations of comet behavior. The surface crumbles easily, and small dust particles become dislodged. The ices and the volatile materials release gases which leak away from the nucleus. The gas pressure is sufficient to move the particles gently away from the comet at speeds of a few meters per second. Sometimes a crack may develop in the conglomerate, in which case the gas will flow from the fissure with greater force and larger fragments can be dislodged from the surface. Sometimes the surface forms a solid crust, and then a considerable amount of gas pressure can build up below the surface. Ultimately the surface must yield to the growing pressure, then a considerable portion of the surface is dislodged. This is sufficient to cause the phenomenon of outbursts; sometimes a comet will show a sudden increase of brightness lasting for a period of a few days, returning again to its normal condition. Collisions in space are also possible. Collisions with an asteroidal fragment would have severe consequences for a cometary nucleus. The soft material would be penetrated by the fragment, and the energy of impact would be released below the surface.

Encke and a few other comets have shown evidence for rocket action. The period of Encke has decreased slightly over its observational history, and the periods of other comets have decreased and increased. Undoubtedly the nucleus of the comet is rotating, because all objects in the solar system show this property. Suppose that when the sun shines on a nucleus, gases escape from cracks in the surface; the gas jet will start shortly after the application of solar heat and will probably last for a short while after the removal of the sunlight. If this is the case, the direction of rotation of the nucleus is important. These gas jets will give the comet a slight impulse which in one sense of rotation will be directed to the outside of the orbit, in the other sense to the inside. Thus under various circumstances a comet might be expected to either accelerate or decelerate by the rocket effect. Although this may seem a rather surprising phenomenon to postulate, it is important to note that no explanation for both acceleration and deceleration is possible on the basis of the gravel-bank model.

The disruption of a comet is not a violent process. It might be expected that if a nucleus were cut in two, a sudden release of gas might be produced from the newly formed surfaces. Comet Biela, for example, did not show any sudden or spectacular changes in the brightness of the coma or tail while it was splitting in two. The breakup must therefore be a fairly gentle process. Gradually a fissure is enlarged as the ices evaporate, until the nucleus is almost a Siamese twin with just a small connecting bridge. Finally the connecting filament evaporates away, and the two halves become independent objects.

New comets shed more dust than old ones. This is rather surprising, for gas is evaporated at each passage around the sun and an old comet might be expected to have lost all its gas. This is not so; it is the long-period and parabolic comets that show the most intense continuous spectrum and hence the greatest amount of flying dust. A short-period comet, making repeated visits to the sun, does not show such strong evidence for dust. As a general rule, the more visits a comet makes to the sun, the more the gaseous spectrum predominates.

It has been suggested by F. L. Whipple that the dust is more compact in an old comet. Maybe over a long period of time processes act to cement the dust together. Certainly toward the end of the life of the nucleus the outer layers have been evaporated, and the remaining portion is the original core. The pressure at the center of a nucleus is not great, perhaps no more than 1 atm for a nucleus 20 km in diameter, yet it may be sufficient to squeeze the fragile dust together.

In this way a long-period comet, making infrequent visits to the sun, sheds the outermost layers, which are finely divided materials. After successive skins are shed, the solid material is less easily dislodged, and there is no supply of fine comet dust to scatter sunlight in the coma and the tail.

Confirmation of this hypothesis is given by observations of meteor streams. The Taurid stream is associated with Comet Encke, a comet that has been evaporated repeatedly. By measuring the deceleration of Taurid meteors it has been shown that the objects are tough, exhibiting little or no fragmentation. Furthermore there is a high proportion of bright meteors in the Taurid stream, indicating that Encke has shed chunks of material that are somewhat larger than average. The Giacobini-Zinner comet, on the other hand, has not been observed for many revolutions and is probably a new comet. Its meteor particles are featherlike, extremely fragile, and probably of very low mean density.

What is the chemical constitution of the nucleus? Here it must be remembered that, except for rocket collection of micrometeorites, very little information is available on the chemistry of the solids. In addition, knowledge of the volatile constituents is limited because not all atoms or molecules produce fluorescent emission lines in the observable spectrum. Thus, knowledge of the chemistry of the nucleus is limited at the present time to little more than intelligent guesswork. Perhaps in the not too distant future a space probe will be launched and placed on a comet nucleus. Then direct analyses can be made and the information relayed to the Earth. Until that time inductive reasoning will have to suffice.

From the presence of NH, OH, and CH it is presumed that frozen ammonia, water, and methane are contained in the nucleus. The free radicals are then produced as the ice evaporates and the vapor is dissociated. It has been suggested that hydrated solids may occur in some quantity. For example, methane and water can produce $CH_4 \cdot 6H_2O$. This idea is very plausible, since the temperature of vaporization of the hydrated methane is high. Thus it is possible to retain this ice during an encounter with the sun much more readily than frozen methane can be retained. At one time it was supposed that free radicals might be contained as such in the nucleus. Although they can be retained to a limited extent in frozen ices, they are very reactive substances and might lead to chemical explosions. In fact, some cometary outbursts and disruptions were once attributed to the explosion of free radicals, an idea that is now considered with disfavor because it is doubted whether the energy of the explosion could be sufficient to cause the observed effects. Subsequently H. C. Urey has suggested that acetylene, C_2H_2, might be present. This is a chemical with violent explosive properties which might be the cause of some cometary outbursts.

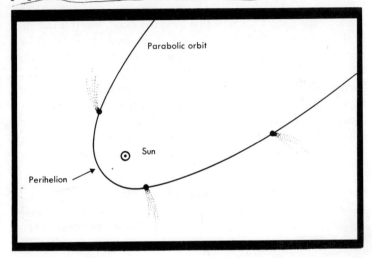

FIGURE 9.1   Orbit of a long-period comet.

So much for the nature of comets. What is their origin? Before going too deeply into this problem, one important fact about their orbits should perhaps be stated. In Chapter 8 it was seen that the majority of comets that visit the sun are in orbits with very long periods, so long in fact that the comet is arbitrarily assigned an infinite period. (A schematic example of a long-period orbit is shown in Figure 9.1.) On the other hand no comet has been observed with a truly hyperbolic orbit, and therefore none has been shown to originate from the region of the distant stars. Now when the period P and semimajor axis a are large, an object will move very slowly in its orbit at aphelion. This can be seen from Kepler's second law and also from Equation (1.2). The majority of comets must therefore spend most of the time in the depths of space, far beyond the orbit of Pluto. A photograph taken at any time would show a large number of comets hovering around the solar system, forming a cloud. This conclusion was first pointed out by J. H. Oort, and the reservoir of comets is known as "Oort's Cloud."

Oort's Cloud is, of course, not a matter of speculation; its existence can be deduced from the known facts of cometary orbits. Discussion of this cloud is only one step from discussion of the origin of the cometary nuclei that form the cloud, but this last step in the argument is left until the end of the book. Oort has shown that we can learn a great deal by considering the few long-period orbits for which very accurate observations and calculations have been made. The reciprocal of the semimajor axis $1/a$ is a very important quantity, because it is proportional to the total energy of a comet in its orbit. It also has the useful property of not becoming infinite for an infinite size orbit; $1/a$ and the total orbital energy become 0 when $a \to \infty$. Table 9.1 gives the number of comets with

TABLE 9.1   LONG PERIOD COMET ORBITS *

$1/a$	NUMBER OF COMETS
$-0.00015--0.00011$	None
$-0.00010--0.00006$	None
$-0.00005--0.00001$	None
$0.00000-+0.00004$	26
$+0.00005-+0.00009$	5
$+0.00010-+0.00014$	1
$+0.00015-+0.00019$	1
$+0.00020-+0.00024$	1
$+0.00025-+0.00029$	1

* Before planetary perturbations.

$1/a$ within intervals of 0.00005. The table is based on 35 comets with a semimajor axis greater than 2,000 AU where the orbit is known with precision. Negative values of $1/a$ would refer to hyperbolic orbits.

The table shows quite clearly the remarkable upper limit to the orbital energy of comets, and demonstrates that most of these long-period comets (26) have $0.0 < 1/a < 0.00004$. The average value of the semimajor axis is 50,000 AU, corresponding to a period of about 11×10^6 years. Of course, although the orbits in Table 9.1 are the very best available, the data are being pushed to the limit, and there is a great uncertainty in the value of the average period. Certain evidence shows that the 26 distant comets probably visited us for the first time in the history of the solar system. Let us examine the evidence for this suggestion.

Every comet that passes between the planets suffers a change in orbital energy and hence in the value of $1/a$. The forces involved are the normal gravitational perturbation of Jupiter, Saturn, etc. On the average the change in $1/a$ is about 0.00065. Thus any comet that starts out in the narrow interval $0.0 < 1/a < 0.00004$ will on the first pass around the sun be moved into a different interval in the table. In fact the average change is so great that the comet would no longer be accommodated within the limits of Table 9.1! All 26 comets did indeed suffer perturbations, and their later orbits no longer show the clear-cut distribution of Table 9.1, so these orbits are pristine paths, untouched by the nefarious planets.

Oort's Cloud may therefore stretch halfway to the nearest star, which is alpha Centauri, at a distance of 24×10^{12} miles, 2.5×10^5 AU. At these great distances the speed of a comet is no more than a few centimeters per second. If it is assumed that all directions of motion are possible, the cloud will contain many circular orbits where the comet never comes near the sun. A slight perturbation from a passing star may be all that is needed to move a comet from the cloud and direct it toward the sun. Oort has shown that if a satisfactory theory is to be constructed, there must be at least 10^{11} comets out there in the "deep-freeze" reservoir.

Detailed calculations have been carried out, but the results will be described briefly in words. New long-period comets are deflected from the cloud by stellar perturbations and come toward the sun at all inclinations to the plane of the solar system. Successive perturbations by the planets alter the orbit drastically; some comets are thrown into hyperbolic orbits and leave the solar system forever, some are reduced in period. Perturbations are more severe for directly moving comets, because these spend more time in the vicinity of a planet. (Perturbations should be carefully distinguished from collisions. A retrograde particle is more likely to suffer a collision with a planet, but a direct particle is more likely to be perturbed.) This probably explains the slight excess of retrograde parabolic orbits noted in Chapter 8. At each return the comet is perturbed sometimes to a smaller orbit, sometimes to a larger orbit. The process is similar to "random walk," and a certain fraction of the comets will change to smaller orbits. Comet Halley is presumably an example of a shortened orbit.

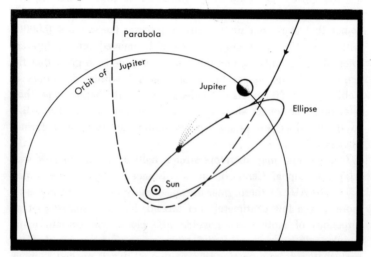

FIGURE 9.2   Orbit of a short-period comet and a schematic illustration of the capture process. (Actually many successive perturbations of Jupiter are required.)

Short-period comets are the result of a drastic perturbation by Jupiter, as illustrated schematically in Figure 9.2. Successive encounters have reduced the periods to about 6 years, and the comets move within the orbit of Jupiter. Presumably this so-called capture process favors direct orbits of low inclination, because these are the predominant characteristics of short-period orbits. Examples of the capture process are known, one being Comet Brooks in 1886, and many comets in this group are seriously affected by Jupiter today. A short-period orbit is usually the "end of the road" for a comet. Repeated heating by the sun disintegrates it, and the orbit is continually shortened by the effects of light pressure, the Poynting-Robertson effect.

How were the billions of icy conglomerates formed, and how did they begin to move and form a part of Oort's Cloud? Any attempt to answer these questions makes inroads far into the realm of speculation. Icy comets may have formed as part of the solar system at the beginning of its history, or on the other hand they may have joined it at a later time. One theory assigns to comets an interstellar origin and therefore falls into the second category of theories. A brief discussion of it follows.

The region between the stars contains atoms, ions, molecules, and solid dust particles. Astrophysical measurements show that the interstellar material probably has the usual cosmic abundances of elements; in every 1,000 atoms, 900 are hydrogen, 99 are helium, and 1 is some heavier element, such as carbon or oxygen. If some of this interstellar material could be scooped up, frozen, and compressed into a ball, it would no doubt make an ideal cometary nucleus. Thus it is tempting to suggest some methods whereby this can take place. One such method is the "gravitational lens" of the sun. As the sun moves through space, its gravitational field will bend the path of interstellar dust and converge it to a point at a distance of several thousand astronomical units behind the sun. It is suggested that the material deflected into a small region of space in this manner can condense and form a cometary nucleus at the distance of Oort's Cloud. If the process can happen once, it is reasonable to suppose that it can continue and that billions of comets can be formed.

Calculations show that condensation will probably not take place and that the theory is invalid. The deflected particles will converge with appreciable kinetic energy which will almost certainly be liberated in the form of heat. The process is quite the reverse of condensation, and it is impossible for an icy conglomerate to form. Most astronomers therefore look for an origin of the comets that is related to the origin of the solar system.

The sun and planets are thought to have condensed from a rotating cloud of dust and gas. The chemical composition was again what is known as the "cosmic mix," though the planets near the sun have been considerably de-iced in the process of formation. It is conceivable that icy conglomerates would condense in the original cloud, provided that the distance from the sun was sufficiently great to avoid evaporation. Three regions have been selected as possibilities.

The icy conglomerates could have formed in the asteroid zone between the orbits of Mars and Jupiter. There is no doubt that more than one planet formed in this region, and meteorites give us evidence that the fragments that reach the Earth are stone or iron. It is just possible for a mass of ice to survive in that region, though we know from the behavior of short-period comets that the life of a comet is not long if its orbit carries it repeatedly near the sun. Oort's Cloud under these circumstances could have been produced by a reverse capture process. Perturbations by Jupiter could deflect cometary nuclei from the asteroid zone out to the fringe of the solar system.

The second possible place of origin is the edge of the solar system, just beyond the orbit of Pluto, at a distance of about 50 or 100 AU from the sun. Perturbations from nearby stars and other unspecified effects are required to deflect some of the cometary nuclei out to the region of Oort's Cloud. The planets in the solar system, of course, revolve in orbits which lie very close to a single plane. The solar system is essentially flat, and the comet nuclei near Pluto would also be expected to move in the plane of the solar system.

The third and most likely place of formation is at the extreme fringe of the solar system, far away from the planets. The icy conglomerates could condense and move after formation in orbits that are tilted at random angles to the solar system. Proponents of this place of origin fortunately do not have to explain how Oort's Cloud came into being as a dynamic structure; it was formed as it is at present, and no perturbations are required to throw the icy conglomerates out to the fringe of the solar system.

Perhaps in the not too distant future it will be possible to cut through the coma of speculation concerning the nature and origin of comets and obtain some solid facts. It would be of great interest to launch a space probe toward the nucleus of a passing comet. The probe could be programmed to bore down into the nucleus, extracting specimens of dust and ice for chemical analysis. It might be possible to do some controlled experiments, such as intensive heating of a portion of the nucleus, or perhaps blasting of the surface materials in an attempt to induce a cometary outburst. Ultimately it might be feasible to produce an icy conglomerate on the Earth and release it to go into orbit around the sun. Observation of the performance of such an artificial comet would provide a great deal of information about the true nature of comets themselves.

at least

Chapter 1

1 Describe and state the differences between a meteor, meteoroid, meteorite, and micrometeorite.

2 Two observers are at the ends of a base line 100 km in length. A meteor is seen directly over the base line at an altitude of 60 deg above the horizon as viewed by both observers. What is the height of the meteor? (*Answer:* 86.6 km, or 86.8 km if the base line is drawn on a curved Earth with radius 6,370 km.)

3 Describe the appearance, physical nature, and possible origin of a fireball.

Chapter 2

1 Describe what happens during the "meteor process" when a meteoroid enters the Earth's atmosphere from interplanetary space.

2 What observational evidence shows that meteoroids are probably loose dustballs?

3 A meteoroid of mass 10^{-3} g with velocity 30 km sec^{-1}, falling vertically, ablates at a height of 100 km in the atmosphere. What is its kinetic energy, what is its brightness, and how could we observe it? (*Answer:* 4.5×10^9 ergs, visual magnitude $+7.4$.)

Chapter 3

1 What advantages does a Super-Schmidt camera have over a standard 35-mm camera? Describe the Super-Schmidt.

2 Derive Equation (3.2). Assume that the camera is pointing directly upward to the zenith and that the meteors are in a layer at a height of 95 km. Use Equation (5.2) and the equation $M_{av} = M - 1$ in your derivation. Assume a circular field of w deg diameter.

3 Discuss the various methods for determining the radiant point of a meteor stream by radar.

Chapter 4

1 "A meteor storm is a spectacular event." Elaborate on this statement and give examples.

2 Give details of the annually recurring meteor streams that can be observed during the months of July and August.

3 Write up the plans for an inexpensive project that you and some assistants could undertake to observe one of the major meteor streams.

Chapter 5

1 Take the antilogarithm of Equation (5.4) and show that the total mass of meteor particles falling over the Earth per day with mass $\geq 10^{-12}$ g is 1.7×10^5 metric tons. (*Hint:* Integrate $m \, dN$ between the limits of $m = 10^{-12}$ g and $m = \infty$; area of Earth's surface $= 5.26 \times 10^8$ km^2, metric ton $= 10^6$ g.)

2 Give several reasons why (*a*) we would be surprised to find a meteor particle in a hyperbolic orbit; (*b*) we do not expect a meteorite to fall from a meteor stream; (*c*) astronomers cannot rely on eye-witness accounts of fireball motion.

3 Give the magnitude distribution of sporadic meteors and fireballs. Explain the significance of the difference between the distributions.

Chapter 6

1 Describe the difficulties that were present, known and unknown, when astronomers attempted to measure the density of the upper atmosphere from observations of meteors.

2 Do meteors affect the troposphere? Discuss the experimental and observational evidence and scientific arguments.

3 Describe experiments that have been made to investigate electromagnetic emission from meteors from very low frequencies (less than 1 cps) up to frequencies of several hundred megacycles.

Chapter 7

1 Prepare a list of simple tests enabling a person to tell whether a specimen is a stone, iron, or stony-iron meteorite, or whether it is an ordinary terrestrial sample.

2 Show how astronomical, chemical, and physical evidence supports the hypothesis that meteorites are fragments from the collision of two or more asteroids.

3 Show that a spherical particle of radius r cm and density 3 g cm^{-3} becomes a micrometeorite if $r \leq 2.5 \times 10^{-4}$ cm. (*Hint:*

Assume an isothermal atmosphere, the density $\rho = \rho_0 e^{-h/H}$ at a height h above the Earth's surface; H is the scale height and ρ_0 is a constant. Assume that the object has decelerated when it encounters its own mass of air and that ablation would normally begin when $\rho = 1.4 \times 10^{-9}$ gm cm^{-3}.)

Chapter 8

1 Describe the appearance, anatomy, and spectrum of an average comet.

2 Describe, with statistics, the families of short-period and long-period comets.

3 Several comets have been notable for some reason or other. Describe a few of them.

Chapter 9

1 What is the physical and chemical nature of a comet? Are there any differences between typical short-period and long-period comets?

2 Take the data of Table 9.1 and plot a histogram to show the number of comets in each interval of $1/a$. Indicate where hyperbolic comets should occur on your diagram. Calculate the number of comets in intervals of a. Draw a new normalized histogram showing the number of comets in intervals of a. Calculate the number of comets in intervals of P using Kepler's harmonic law (see Chapter 1). Plot a normalized histogram in intervals of P. Does Oort's Cloud have a sharp outer boundary?

3 You are in charge of designing a deep space probe to explore a comet. Give the payload and maneuvers of the probe that you would specify in order to obtain maximum information about comets, giving particular attention to the uncertainties in the various theories relating to comets.